AIR POLLUTION EXPERIMENTS FOR JUNIOR AND SENIOR HIGH SCHOOL SCIENCE CLASSES

Second Edition

Edited by
DONALD C. HUNTER, P.E.
and
HENRY C. WOHLERS, PH.D.

EDUCATION COMMITTEE
MID-ATLANTIC STATES SECTION
AIR POLLUTION CONTROL ASSOCIATION

TABLE OF CONTENTS

PREFACE TO THE SECOND EDITION

Demand for copies of the first edition of "Air Pollution Experiments for Junior and Senior High School Science Classes" following publication in 1969 prompted the start toward this second edition. The manual has grown to 38 experiments, comprising a group of exercises which can be selected according to the interests of the student. All are true experiments; positive results depend on the experimenter and on the nature of the experiment. For example, the student may run into a blank wall if the polluting substance he plans to measure is not present in sufficient quantity in the total gas sampled. Here the student's thinking apparatus should come into play to modify the conditions of the experiment so that a measurable quantity of the pollutant can be absorbed or adsorbed.

(continued)

The authors and editors realize that some educators will consider portions of the experimental work too difficult for the high school level. The intent is to stretch the student mind, and we believe that students who are motivated will find the work well within their capabilities. Quantitative excellence is not expected. That will come later with experience.

Abatement of air pollution has so often resulted in another waste disposal problem that several experiments have been included, indicating how some waste products can be put to good use. The authors and editors have tried to stimulate student thought on (1) possible improvement of the economics involved in abatement processed, (2) use of recovery and recycling to conserve the earth's resources for future generations, and (3) use of clean sources of energy which do not deplete our resources or produce pollution.

While preparing this edition, it occurred to us that many of the experiments would be taking a majority of students far ahead of the teaching of scientific theory, with the result they could be learning practice first and theory second, and that this might be good. Who hasn't had trouble solving right triangle problems after first being taught by rote that the square on the hypotenuse of a right triangle is equal to the sum of the squares on the other two sides? Wouldn't it be better for the teacher to provide students with the triangle or the carpenter's square first and then to guide them gradually toward the realization that the foregoing relationship exists? Wouldn't it help students to a clearer understanding of calculus to give them first a practical frame of reference—for example, how calculus is involved every time they pull away from a traffic light? Why teach mechanical advantage and bending moments before the student has had the opportunity to learn how levers of different design operate? Shouldn't the student learn from his own experience why the farther his force is applied from the fulcrum the less it has to be to move a given weight at the other end of the lever?

The editors are aware that such heresy will make waves if teaching is still done as it was when they were in school. But, if we pause to think about it, we all learned to walk and to make ourselves understood in a mighty complex language without being taught. The teacher who stimulates thought through observation of practical processes may be the one whose students acquire the better education. A "student" is defined by *Webster's New Collegiate Dictionary* as a learner and an attentive and systematic observer. Observation has been encouraged in each experiment presented herewith.

Donald C. Hunter, P.E.
Henry C. Wohlers, Ph.D.
Editors

Education Committee
Mid-Atlantic States Section
Air Pollution Control Association
February 1, 1972

PREFACE TO THE FIRST EDITION

This manual of experiments for the high school science classroom is designed to acquaint students at both the junior and senior levels with some of the problems and effects of air pollution and some of the practical means of overcoming them. The difficulties recruiters of college graduates are experiencing in finding men and women trained in the disciplines of air pollution control emphasize the need to acquaint boys and girls during their formative years with some of the interesting aspects of a career which can be highly rewarding personally as well as essential to public health.

Experiments have been selected and designed, insofar as possible, to utilize equipment and instruments which most high schools would have in their chemistry, physics, or biology laboratories. Some unusual pieces of equipment can be built by the students from readily available, inexpensive materials. Where purchase is the more practical solution, low cost has been kept in mind in the selections suggested.

Some experiments require exposure of basic components to outdoor air for a month. Some require laboratory work to be spread over several 40-minute periods. Convenient pauses are possible and in some instances are indicated.

The editors are indebted to the State of California, Department of Public Health, for permission to make use of "Experiments for the Science Classroom Based on Air Pollution Problems." The California format was considered excellent and was adopted. Some experiments applicable also to East Coast conditions, were used without much change. We have also drawn on "Air Pollution Experiments—High School Edition," published by Cooperative Extension Service, College of Agriculture and Environmental Science, Rutgers—The State University. The authors have used Air Pollution by A. C. Stern and various publications of the Public Health Service as source material.

The American Chemical Society and McGraw-Hill, Inc. have graciously permitted use of copyrighted material.

We are grateful to Mr. Thomas Moran, Division of Laboratories and Research, New York State Department of Health, for his patience and ingeniousness in developing, building, and testing some of the unusual pieces of equipment. Other members of the Division of Laboratories and Research are to be commended for their help in testing the chemistry of some of the experiments. Authors of individual experiments are noted at the end of each.

Donald C. Hunter, P.E.
Henry C. Wohlers, Ph.D.
Editors

Education Committee
Mid-Atlantic States Section
Air Pollution Control Association
November 1, 1968

AUTHORS

Daniel M. Barolo, P.E.

Sanitary Engineer, Division of Air Resources, New York State Department of Environmental Conservation, Albany, New York 12201

David M. Benforado, P.E.

Specialist, Environmental Engineering and Pollution Control, 3M Company, St. Paul, Minn. 55101

Serouya Benhayem

Instructor, Center for Environmental Studies, Temple University, Philadelphia, Pa. 19140

Allen D. Brandt, Ph.D.*

Manager, Environmental Quality Control, Bethlehem Steel Corporation, Bethlehem, Pa. 18016

Eileen G. Brennan, M.Sc.

Assoc. Research Professor, Department of Plant Pathology, College of Agriculture and Environmental Science, Rutgers—The State University, New Brunswick, N.J. 08903

William M. Delaware

Sanitary Engineer, Division of Air Resources, New York State Department of Environmental Conservation, Albany, N.Y. 12201

Donald E. Gower, P.E.

Chief, Continuous Air Monitoring Section, Division of Air Resources, New York State Department of Environmental Conservation, Albany, N.Y. 12201

James R. Griggs

Student, Avoca Community High School, Avoca, Iowa 51521

Frederick B. Higgins, Jr., Ph.D., P.E.

Asst. Professor of Environmental Engineering, Drexel University, Philadelphia, Pa. 19104

Eric M. Holt

Sanitary Engineer, Division of Air Resources, New York State Department of Environmental Conservation, Albany, N.Y. 12201

Donald C. Hunter, P.E.

Chief, Manual Air Monitoring Section, Division of Air Resources, New York State Department of Environmental Conservation, Albany, N.Y. 12201

Jay S. Jacobson, Ph.D.

Plant Physiologist, Boyce Thompson Institute for Plant Research, Inc., Yonkers, N.Y. 10701

Ida A. Leone, M.Sc.

Assoc. Research Professor, Department of Plant Pathology, College of Agriculture & Environmental Science, Rutgers, The State University, New Brunswick, N.J. 08903

Robert L. Marino

Scientist, Division of Air Resources, New York State Department of Environmental Conservation, Albany, N.Y. 12201

---

*Deceased

Thomas J. Moran
   Laboratory Equipment Designer, Division of Laboratories and Research, New York State Department of Health, Albany, N.Y. 12208

David J. Romano, P.E.
   Chief, Technical Assistance Section, Division of Air Resources, New York State Department of Environmental Conservation, Albany, N.Y. 12201

Victor H. Sussman, P.E.
   Director, Division of Air Pollution Control, Commonwealth of Pennsylvania, Harrisburg, Pa.

Russell E. Thurn
   Product Quality Coordination, Chevron Oil, Perth Amboy, N.J. 08861

Leonard H. Weinstein, Ph.D.
   Program Director, Environmental Biology, Boyce Thompson Institute for Plant Research, Inc., Yonkers, N.Y. 10701

Henry C. Wohlers, Ph.D.
   Professor of Environmental Sciences, Drexel University, Philadelphia, Pa. 19104

PARTICIPANTS

Michael Bolduc
   Supervisor, Air Pollution Control, 3M Company, St. Paul, Minn. 55101

William Colver
   Graduate Student, Drexel University, Philadelphia, Pa. 19104

Donald A. Corliss
   Graduate Student, University of Minnesota, Minneapolis, Minn. 55455

A. Dressler
   Senior Laboratory Technician, 3M Company, St. Paul, Minn. 55101

Ross F. McCurdy
   Graduate Student, University of Minnesota, Minneapolis, Minn. 55455

John M. Joyce
   Senior Engineering Technician, Division of Air Resources, New York State Department of Environmental Conservation, Albany, N.Y. 12201

Thomas J. Moran
   Laboratory Equipment Designer, Division of Laboratories and Research, New York State Department of Health, Albany, N.Y. 12208

Harold J. Paulus, Ph.D.
   Professor, School of Public Health, University of Minnesota, Minneapolis, Minn. 55455

INTRODUCTION

Man, his animals, and his vegetation live in an ocean of air. Man and most other animals can survive a considerable number of days without food and a few days without water. But, none of them can survive much more than a few minutes without air. An adult of the species homo sapiens must inhale about 400 cubic feet of air each day to obtain the necessary oxygen to sustain life. Air entering the respiratory tract must not menace health.

Pure, dry air contains by volume 20.92% oxygen, 78.14% nitrogen, 0.04% carbon dioxide, and 0.9% argon and trace amounts of other noble gases. For practical purposes we usually lump the inert gases with the nitrogen and consider air as being 20.9% oxygen and 79.1% nitrogen; water vapor in natural air may be present up to the saturation level. Any other substances in air, whether solid particles, gases, or vapors, are contaminants. Some create economic loss, some are detrimental to the health of people, livestock and vegetation, some interfere with the general welfare and enjoyment of living, and others cause no adverse effect at our present stage of knowledge.

Air pollution is of two general types—natural and man-made.

Natural pollution consists of substances such as pollens and spores expelled by flowers and fungi and natural dusts picked up by the wind. These substances, especially ragweed pollen, can be extremely distressing to those who are allergic. Surveys have indicated that something like 10 to 15% of the population are allergic to ragweed pollen. This allergy results in what is commonly known as hayfever. It can develop into chronic asthma and sometimes death.

Man-made pollution results from man's activities. It has both industrial and personal origins. Combustion, such as for industrial heat and power, and various industrial processes are examples. Individual home heating furnaces, motor vehicles, and solid waste disposal are sources due to individual activity.

Local, state, and federal government agencies have been and are endeavoring to reduce the quantities of polluting materials discharged into the atmosphere. Significant reductions for adequately clean air will probably require many years. Thus, there will be a continuing need for engineers, physicians, scientists, and administrators educated in the various disciplines involved in air pollution control.

There can be no compromise with those contaminants menacing human health. Standards must be and in many states are being set at levels which will not be detrimental to the health of either the very young or the aged, who are usually the most sensitive. In some instances, certain types of sensitive vegetation are affected more quickly than human health, and thus they become good indicators of approaching problems.

The following experiments have been selected to acquaint students with some of the problems encountered in air pollution control work and with some of the means of overcoming them. The actual problems encountered in air pollution work are usually more highly complex than those presented in experiments contained in this manual. It is hoped the high school teacher will emphasize the point that measuring air pollution and its effects is not always as simple as these experiments may indicate.

It is also hoped that additional experiments, whose omission from this manual is made obvious by continued progress in this field of study, will be brought to the attention of the editors. These will be evaluated for possible inclusion in the next edition of the manual.

The Editors

EXPERIMENT NO. 1

Effect of Air Pollution on Nylon

I. Object

1. To demonstrate the effect of certain types of air pollution on an everyday item of wearing apparel.
2. To demonstrate one way by which air pollution can have a direct bearing on family living cost.

II. Suitability and Usefulness

1. The experiment provides a direct, and dramatic example of one manner by which air pollution can affect everyday living.
2. It is suitable for a demonstration at both the junior and senior high school levels.

III. Theory

The usable life of nylon goods, particularly women's hose, is often shortened by air pollution. Instances of severe nylon hose deterioration have been reported in the United States, Canada, England, and aboard some ships. The prime destroyer has been called "acidic soot." The known probable destructive agents of nylon hose are: (1) hot particles contained in smoke, (2) soot laden with sulfuric acid, (3) acid aerosols, (4) nitrogen oxides, (5) phenolic particulates and aldehydes from internal combustion engines, and (6) solvent vapors and droplets.

IV. Equipment

1. Good quality (15 denier) nylon hose, cut to proper size to fit the mounting frame.
2. Standard Polaroid slide mount #633, size $3\frac{1}{4}'' \times 4''$ (available at local camera stores).
3. Sheet metal frame or wood block (2 required) to hold the slide mount so that the air can come in contact with both sides of the nylon.
4. Slide projector and screen; or, low-power microscope or magnifying glass.

V. Procedure

1. Cut a square piece of the nylon hose of sufficient size for the Polaroid slide mount.
2. Stretch it over one half of the mount and glue it in place between the two halves of the mount.
3. Prepare a second sample in the same manner.
4. Place the mounted nylon in the holders in an unobstructed and safe place on the school roof so that the nylon is held in a horizontal position.
5. Leave one nylon sample exposed for 30 days; the second should be exposed for 90 days.
6. At the end of its exposure period, take each sample to the laboratory and examine it for broken threads. This can be made easier by projecting the mounted sample on a screen or by examining it with a low-power microscope or magnifying glass.
7. A sample stored inside for the same period may be used as a control for comparison.
8. For comparative purposes, students may wish to expose some samples without shelter and some in the louvered shelter (Exp. No. 3).

VI. Records

1. Record the number of "breaks" per day of exposure for each sample.

VII. References

1. Interstate Air Pollution Effects Surveillance Network; Field Investigations Section, Abatement Branch, Division of Air Pollution, Robert A. Taft Sanitary Engineering Center, 4676 Columbia Parkway, Cincinnati, Ohio 45226.

VIII. Prepared by Donald C. Hunter

EXPERIMENT NO. 2

Effect of Air Pollution on Dyed Fabrics

I. Object

1. To demonstrate that certain types of air pollution can cause fading of dyed fabrics.
2. To demonstrate that air pollution can increase family cost due to fading of dyed fabrics.

II. Suitability and Usefulness

1. The experiment can be used as a demonstration for either junior or senior high school students.
2. The experiment teaches the economic effects of air pollution as reflected in family living cost.

III. Theory

Stability of colors in dyed fabrics is extremely variable. Some of the causes of color fading are strong sunlight, washing, heat, and humidity. Recently attention has been given to air pollution as a cause of fading. Oxides of nitrogen and ozone are suspected as being the air contaminants responsible.

The American Association of Textile Chemists and Colorists (AATCC) has developed two experimental standard dyed fabrics, one of which is sensitive to nitrogen oxides and the other to ozone. Exposure of these two standard fabrics will provide a rough measure or index of the concentration of nitrogen oxides or ozone in the atmosphere.

Simultaneous, similar exposure of samples of dyed fabric from home to contrast with the experimental fabrics should provide a rough measure of the economic loss your family may be experiencing from the fading of dyes as a result of air pollution.

IV. Equipment

1. Louvered shelter, about 8″ × 8″ × 8″. This can be the same shelter as used for the experiment on exposure of rubber. (See "Effect of Ozone on Rubber.")
2. AATCC Gas Fading Control Fabric (fastness to oxides of nitrogen), in rolls 2″ wide × 10 yards. Available from Test Fabrics, Inc., 55 Vandam Street, New York, New York 10013. Cost—2 rolls for $5.00.
3. AATCC Fabric for Color Fastness to Ozone, in rolls 2″ wide × 10 yards. Available from Test Fabrics, Inc., 55 Vandam Street, New York, New York 10013. Cost—2 rolls for $7.50.
4. Cardboard for holding fabric samples during exposure.
5. Contact adhesive to hold fabric samples in mounting frames.

V. Procedure

1. Prepare a mount for each test sample of fabric by cutting a 2″ square window in a piece of 2¾″ square cardboard. (Photographic mounting frames may be used.)
2. Place a 2″ × 2¾″ sample of the fabric to be tested over the window and fasten each end to the cardboard, using the contact adhesive.
3. Identify each sample.
4. Hang each sample in the louvered shelter to avoid strong sunlight striking it. The shelter should have been placed at an unobstructed and safe spot on the roof of your school. It should be supported on a box, or similar support, about 2½ to 3 feet above the roof surface.
5. At the end of a 90-day exposure period, take the exposed samples to the laboratory and compare color brightness with that on the unexposed fabric, which has been suitably sealed and stored to prevent contact with atmosphere.

VI. Records

1. Record your observations, and try to rate each sample for degree of color fading. Can you estimate the amount that fabric color degradation due to air pollution may be costing your family each year?

VII. References

1. Interstate Air Pollution Effects Surveillance Network; Field Investigations Section, Abatement Branch, Division of Air Pollution, Robert A. Taft Sanitary Engineering Center, 4676 Columbia Parkway, Cincinnati, Ohio 45226.

VIII. Prepared by Donald C. Hunter

EXPERIMENT NO. 3

Effect of Air Pollution on Rubber

I. Object

1. To demonstrate the effect of ozone and other oxidizing substances in the atmosphere on rubber.

II. Suitability and Usefulness

1. Can be used as a demonstration project.

2. Makes the observer more aware of the economic loss resulting from this type of air pollution.

3. By using an arbitrary rating system for the amount of damage occurring to rubber samples during a given period of time, students can make a rough determination of the oxidizing properties of pollution present in the atmosphere.

III. Theory and Background

Rubber is one of the most important naturally occurring chemical materials. Hundreds of articles essential to our modern civilization are manufactured from it. It was probably used as early as the eleventh century, and several centuries later was named by Joseph Priestly because of its ability to *rub out* or erase pencil marks. Its technical use began in 1761 when rubber tubing was first produced. The discovery of vulcanization by Charles Goodyear in 1839 made possible the rapid growth of the rubber industry and its most important product, the automobile tire.

Natural rubber (india rubber or caoutchouc) is the elastic solid appearing as a colloidal suspension in the milky exudation, or latex, of certain tropical trees. Many trees, shrubs, vines, and plants produce latex, but the plantation tree *Hevea brasiliensis* is the most important of the rubber industry. The rubber particles represent about 35% of the latex, and are coagulated and removed from the latex by chemical processing, such as treatment with acetic acid.

Rubber is naturally a polymer. A polymer is a substance in which many small molecules are linked together in chain, or other, configuration to form giant molecules. The rubber molecule is made up of many small molecules or units of C_5H_8 (isoprene) linked together. The size of the rubber molecule and its configuration are not definitely known. Values for the molecular weight of rubber range from 5,000 to 200,000, although the molecular weight of one C_5H_8 unit is only 68.

The rubber molecule is an unsaturated hydrocarbon. The term "unsaturated" is used to describe the situation in which there are not enough atoms of hydrogen or other elements present to satisfy the four valence bonds of each carbon atom. (This is the same "unsaturated" and "polyunsaturated" you have heard so much about on T.V. commercials.) Thus, in the molecule C_5H_8 or any multiple of it, two of the carbon atoms in each C_5H_8 unit have to be linked by a double bond. For illustrative purposes only, two possible configurations are included here to show how the double bond might occur:

(1)

(2)

Ozone, although present in the atmosphere in only very small amounts, vigorously attacks the carbon-carbon double bonds, with eventual molecular chain-breaking. The attack is most serious when the rubber is exposed while stretched, folded, or otherwise stressed. The physical effect is readily visible as cracking and checking of the rubber. At the same time, its ability to be stretched and then return to its original shape and size is greatly reduced.

Research has indicated that the prime cause of cracking and checking of rubber exposed to the atmosphere is ozone and that light, heat, and moisture are secondary, contributing factors. Light is not necessary for ozone to have its own effect on rubber. These effects occur even in the dark. The problem has been partially overcome by development of some of the synthetic rubbers, which are not actually rubbers but are compounds developed to substitute for natural rubber.

Most of the synthetic rubbers are much more resistant to ozone because of greater saturation of the hydrocarbon molecules (less or no double bonding of adjacent carbon atoms). Synthetics such as neoprene, butyl, Thiokol, silicone, Hypalon, and polyacrylate rubbers are most resistant. But synthetics based on butadiene or isoprene and the nitrile rubbers are more like natural rubber in their lower resistance to ozone. Special materials have been added to commercial rubbers to minimize the effects of exposure to ozone.

IV. Equipment

1. A small shelter box, an 8″ cube, with louvered sides in which to expose a stretched strip of rubber without strong sunlight striking the rubber. One side of the shelter should be hinged to form a door.

2. Rubber strips, 5/16″ × 2″, cut from 9″ × 9″ × 1/16″ sheets of ozone-sensitive test pads, Goodyear Specification No. 563–27303. This special rubber should be ordered from Goodyear Tire and Rubber Co., 1356 Tennessee Avenue, Cincinnati, Ohio or from the nearest Goodyear District Sales Office. The special rubber should be the same as supplied for U. S. Public Health Service order #20374 of April 27, 1965, and the order should be marked for the attention of Mr. B. L. Mattingly at the Goodyear Los Angeles plant. Cost—about $1.00 per 9″ × 9″ sheet.

3. 5/8″ Medium Binder Clip, IPKO #5 or IDL #50, available from any office supply store. Two required.

4. Bottle for unexposed rubber strips; #10–5935 bottle, vial Titeseal; 3-dram capacity, 65-mm height, 19-mm diameter; available from local laboratory supplier or drug store.

5. Lead weight, with a hook or chain attached at one end to put the rubber strip under constant tension. Weight, including lower binder clip, should be 375 grams.

V. Procedure

1. Place the louvered shelter box at a convenient,

safe, and unobstructed spot on the roof of your school. It should preferably be set on a box or other support to keep it about 2½ to 3 feet above the roof surface.

2. Attach the upper clip to one end of a 5/16″ × 2″ rubber strip, gripping the rubber ¼″ from the end, and hang the clip from a hook in the roof of the louvered shelter.

3. Attach the lower clip to the other end of the rubber strip, again gripping the rubber ¼″ from the end. (The length of rubber strip between the clips will then be 1½″.) Hang the lead weight from the lower clip, putting the rubber between clips under tension. Close the door of the shelter.

4. After 7 days of exposure to atmosphere passing through the shelter, remove the rubber strip and examine it, while under the same tension, for degree of cracking or checking. Note any degradation in its ability to be stretched and then return to its original length from that of an unexposed strip. (Note: If exposure of 7 days is not sufficient to cause noticeable cracking or other degradation, the period of exposure should be extended.)

5. If several successive experiments are conducted over a period of weeks, students can apply an arbitrary numerical rating to the degree of degradation found, and can in turn apply a rating to the air with respect to the amount of ozone and any similar oxidizing materials in the air for successive exposure periods.

VI. References

1. Interstate Air Pollution Effects Surveillance Network; Field Investigations Section, Abatement Branch, Division of Air Pollution, Robert A. Taft Sanitary Engineering Center, Cincinnati, Ohio 45226; November 1, 1965.

2. Deterioration of Materials; edited by G. A. Greathouse and C. J. Wessel; Reinhold Publishing Corp., 1954.

3. An Outline of Organic Chemistry; Degering, Nelson, and Harrod; Barnes & Noble, Inc., New York, New York; 1937.

4. The Effects of Photochemical Oxidants on Materials; L. S. Jaffe; Journal of the Air Pollution Control Association, 4400 Fifth Avenue, Pittsburgh, Pennsylvania 15213; June 1967.

VII. Prepared by Donald C. Hunter

EXPERIMENT NO. 4

Effect of Air Pollution on Silver

I. Object

1. To determine whether pollution present in outdoor air has any effect on the appearance of silver after exposure.

II. Suitability and Usefulness

1. Good as a demonstration project for high school students.

2. Provides a measure of the silver tarnishing properties of the air.

III. Theory and Background

You are all familiar with the problem your mother has from time to time with the tarnishing of silver. She gets out a soft cloth and the jar of silver polish, and by expenditure of considerable elbow grease restores the surface of the family silverware to its original brightness.

Sulfides, particularly hydrogen sulfide (H_2S), have the property of reacting with silver to form black silver sulfide (Ag_2S) which we call "tarnish." In addition to its blackness, tarnish is dull. Therefore amount of tarnish can be measured quite accurately by changes in the reflectance of light from the surface of the silverware. This can be done with an instrument known as a reflectometer, which indicates the amount of light reflected from a surface by a voltage signal on a dial or recorder chart. A less accurate measurement of the amount of tarnish can be made by visual observation and comparison with an untarnished piece.

Sulfur compounds from many types of sources are usually in the air to a greater or lesser degree, depending on the amount of local activity. Some of these compounds are emitted as sulfides; others may be changed to sulfides after being emitted. Some food products are responsible for tarnish within the home. Other sources are fuel combustion and some industrial processes.

By exposing a piece of silver out-of-doors, we can get a measure of the tarnishing properties of the air.

IV. Equipment

1. A piece of silverware, broken knife or fork, which might have been discarded at home. Or, the school might purchase a piece of 6-inch diameter silverplate which could be cut into several individual samples.

2. Silver polish and soft cloth.

3. Reflectometer, if available.

4. Small glass jar.

5. Saran wrap.

V. Procedure

If a reflectometer is available, the reflectance of the sample will be measured before and after exposure. If amount of tarnish is to be determined by visual comparison, two samples will be needed— one to be exposed to polluted air, and the other to be stored in a sulfide-free atmosphere.

Proceed as follows:

1. Using a good silver polish according to the manufacturer's instructions, polish all samples to equivalent brightness. This will represent "zero" tarnish.

2. a. If a reflectometer is used, measure the reflectance of the sample and then place it outdoors in a convenient location so that it will be exposed to the ambient air for 30 days.

   b. If visual comparison is to be used in measuring amount of tarnish, use two samples, exposing one outdoors for 30 days and the other in a small glass jar sealed with Saran wrap.

3. After exposing the samples for 30 days, bring them to the laboratory and determine the reflectance, or compare the exposed sample with the one kept in the jar.

4. Compute precent loss of reflectance, or estimate amount of tarnish from visual comparison.

VI. Records

Keep neat and accurate records of your observations.

VII. References

1. Interstate Air Pollution Effects Surveillance Network; Field Investigations Section, Abatement Branch, Air Pollution Control Office, Environmental Protection Agency, Research Triangle Park, N.C.

VIII. Prepared by Donald C. Hunter

EXPERIMENT NO. 5

Effect of Some Gaseous Air Pollutants on the Ciliary Motion in the Frog Buccal Cavity

I. Object

1. To demonstrate the effect of sulfur dioxide, ozone, and cigarette smoke on the ciliary activity in the buccal cavity of the frog.

II. Suitability and Usefulness

1. In man, cilia are an integral part of the respiratory defense mechanism. This experiment demonstrates how ciliary motion can be affected by various gaseous air pollutants.

2. Good as a biology laboratory experiment and demonstration.

III. Theory

The function of the cilia in the frog is to push food particles toward the stomach. The direction of the ciliary motion is, therefore, from the mouth toward the stomach. In man, however, the main function of the cilia is to transport mucus from the respiratory tract.

The direction of human ciliary motion is the following:

$$\text{LUNG} \xrightarrow[\substack{\text{mucus transported} \\ \text{by cilia}}]{\text{Direction of}} \text{ESOPHAGUS} \xleftarrow[\substack{\text{mucus transported} \\ \text{by cilia}}]{\text{Direction of}} \text{NOSE}$$

The mucociliary system, one of the body's most important defenses against respiratory infection and injury, extends from the anterior portion of the nasal turbinate to the respiratory bronchioles in man. The function of the respiratory cilia, together with its overlying blanket of mucus, is to keep the airway surface clean both in the upper and lower respiratory tracts. The beating of the cilia keeps the blanket of mucus, along with trapped foreign material, in continuous movement toward the orifice of the esophagus where it is swallowed or expectorated. Ambient temperature, dryness, and various chemical irritants, including many environmental air pollutants, may have deleterious effects on the activity of the cilia and result in a change in the viscosity of the mucus. As a consequence of such poor mucociliary clearance, bac-

teria and other harmful agents trapped in the mucous blanket are allowed adequate time to penetrate the underlying mucosa.

By determining the effect of air pollutants on ciliary motion in the frog buccal cavity, we can get an idea of the manner in which the cilia in man are affected by these pollutants.

IV. Equipment

1. Frogs.
2. Frog board and pins.
3. Student dissecting kit containing scissors and straight needle.
4. Amphibian Ringer's solution.*
5. Exposure chamber (desiccator with lid tubulation).
6. Sulfur dioxide or ozone source (lecture size cylinder with needle valve for SO_2; UV lamp for ozone).
7. Non-filter cigarette.
8. Millimeter scale.
9. Stopwatch.
10. Ball formed from putty or kneaded eraser to less than 0.5 mm in diameter.
11. Plastic wash bottle, 250 ml.
12. Needles and assorted hypodermic syringes.
13. Tubing, preferably Tygon.
14. Ventilated laboratory hood.

V. Procedure

A. Preparation of Frog and Determination of Pre-Exposure Activity of Cilia

---

*Amphibian Ringer's Solution: To 6.5 grams sodium chloride, 0.14 gram potassium chloride, 0.16 gram calcium chloride ($CaCl_2 \cdot 2H_2O$), 0.2 gram sodium bicarbonate, and 0.01 gram monosodium phosphate, add sufficient distilled water to prepare 1 liter.

Note: Step 1 should be performed by the teacher if students are inexperienced in the pithing technique.

1. Destroy the frog's brain and spinal cord by pithing. (See description of procedure below.)
2. Pin the frog's extremities to the frog board, dorsal side down.
3. Expose the esophagus by removing the lower jaw and tongue with a scissors.
4. Very gently wash the buccal cavity with Amphibian Ringer's solution; excessive moisture can be absorbed with a paper napkin.
5. With a straight needle, gently place the putty ball* on the buccal surface directly posterior to the vomerine teeth (Fig 5-1a).
6. After the ball moves a distance of 2 millimeters start the stopwatch.
7. After the ball has traveled a distance of 5 millimeters more toward the glottis, stop the stopwatch.
8. Remove the ball with the aid of the straight needle and wash to remove mucus.
9. Using the following equation, determine the velocity as millimeters/minute:

$$\frac{5 \text{ mm.} \times 60 \text{ sec.}}{\text{Seconds to travel 5 mm.}} = \text{Velocity of the ball (mm/minute)}$$

10. Repeat steps No. 4 through No. 9 a few times using the same ball. The average value of these velocities is the average velocity for that ball in a pre-exposed animal.
11. Wash the buccal cavity with the Amphibian Ringer's solution and place the frog in the exposure chamber containing ambient air; allow the frog to be exposed for five minutes.
12. Remove the frog from the chamber.
13. Repeat steps No. 4 through No. 10 to obtain the average velocity of the ball in the post-exposed animal.
14. Repeat above steps (No. 1 through No. 13) with additional frogs, using the exposure chamber to which is added 50 ppm sulfur dioxide, 10 ppm ozone, or cigarette smoke as described below. (Because of the short exposure periods, higher concentrations of the gases are required than that which is usually found in ambient air.)

*For each animal all (pre- and post-exposure) velocity determinations should be done with the same ball.

Procedure for pithing the frog brain and spinal cord:

1. Hold the frog so its forelimbs are clamped between the third and fourth fingers and the head is between the third and second fingers.
2. Place the thumb against the frog's back to insure a good hold and allow for flexation of the head.
3. Bend the head slightly forward and note a slight depression at the base of the cranium which overlies the *foramen magnum*.
4. Insert the straight needle into the foramen keeping the needle axis in line with the head.
5. Push the needle into the cranial cavity.
6. Rotate the needle in a conical motion to completely destroy the brain.
7. To pith the spinal cord, without removing the needle from the cranial cavity insert the needle into the spinal canal almost the entire length of the canal.
8. Rotate the needle between your fingers to completely destroy the spinal cord.
9. Frog should be flabby, and experiment can begin.

B. Exposure of Frog to Sulfur Dioxide and Ozone

Volume of the exposure chamber can be determined by filling it with a measured amount of water. Dry the chamber before adding the gases.

1. Attach one end of tubing (approx. 6″ long) to the needle valve of the lecture size gas cylinder; allow the other end of tubing to rest in a beaker of water. (Fig. 5-1b)
2. Open the cylinder valve and gradually open the needle valve until bubbles emerge from the water. Allow the gas to flow in this manner for a few minutes to flush the tubing.
3. With a needle attached to a hypodermic syringe, puncture the tubing and withdraw sufficient volume of gas to produce the desired concentration in the chamber volume. See example:

$$S = \frac{V \times C}{1,000,000}$$

S = Volume of pollutant (100% concentration) to withdraw from lecture bottle or gas generator (Step 3)

V = Dessicator volume in ml. (e.g., 8,000 ml.)

C = Desired final concentration of pollutant in parts per million (ppm.) (e.g., 50 ppm.)

$$S = \frac{8,000 \times 50}{1,000,000} = 0.4 \text{ ml.}$$

4. Through a rubber stopper in the chamber tubulation, inject the gaseous contents of the syringe (Fig. 5-1c) into the chamber.

5. Flush the syringe a few times to ensure adequate mixing within the chamber.

Caution: High concentrations of sulfur dioxide and ozone are dangerous if inhaled. Be sure all apparatus is under a well ventilated laboratory hood when using these gases.

Note: Ozone can be produced fresh with an ultraviolet lamp (GE 4-S-11) mounted in a small opaque enclosure having an air inlet and a valved discharge nipple. The lamp must have proper ballast, such as GE 89-G-504, wired in series to reduce the voltage. (A 100-watt incandescent lamp makes a suitable substitute if the specified ballast is not available.) Concentration of ozone produced can be determined by the method described in Experiment No. 7. The ozone-air mixture will have to be pushed out of the ozone generator by a small pump so that a sample can be obtained from the outlet tubing with the syringe.

C. Exposure of Frog to Cigarette Smoke

1. Connect a non-filter cigarette to a 20-ml. hypodermic syringe with a short piece of tubing.

2. Light the cigarette, and draw about 20 ml. of smoke into the syringe fairly rapidly.

3. Proceed with steps 4 through 5 of B.

VI. Calculations

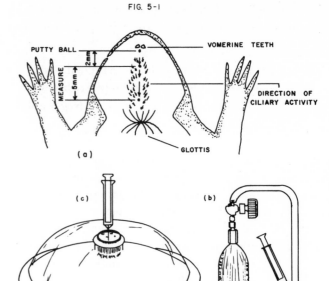

FIG. 5-1

DRAWINGS by JOSEPHINE R. SMITH

VII. References

1. Ballenger, J., "Disease of Nose, Throat, and Ear," 11th edition, Lea and Febiger, Philadelphia, 1969, pp. 1–21.

2. Dalhman, Tore, "Mucous Flow and Ciliary Activity in the Trachea of Healthy Rats and Rats Exposed to Respiratory Irritant Gases," *Acta Physiologica Scandinavica,* Vol. 36, Supplement 123, 1956.

3. Fenn, W. O., and Rahn, H. (editors), "Handbook of Physiology," Volume 1, American Physiological Society, Washington, D.C., 1964, p. 321.

$$\frac{\text{Velocity (pre exposure)} - \text{Velocity (post exposure)}}{\text{Velocity (pre exposure)}} \times 100 = \pm \% \text{ reduction in ciliary activity}$$

after exposure to ambient air, SO_2, O_3, or cigarette smoke

Compare the % reduction in ciliary activity of the control (exposed to ambient air) with the % reduction in ciliary activity resulting from exposure to sulfur dioxide, ozone, or cigarette smoke.

VIII. Prepared by Serouya Benhayem

EXPERIMENT NO. 6

Ozone Damage to Vegetation

I. Object

1. To become familiar with symptoms of ozone toxicity on vegetation.
2. To observe the relative susceptibility of several plant species to ozone damage.
3. To determine the ozone dosage that injures plants as compared to a non-living target, rubber.

II. Suitability and Usefulness

1. Can serve as a demonstration project.
2. Can illustrate the nature and extent of ozone damage to different plant receptors.
3. Can be used as a starting point for a more detailed study of ozone-damaged plant tissue.

III. Theory

Some authorities term ozone the pollutant responsible for the greatest amount of plant damage in the U.S. It is a secondary air pollutant; that is, most of it is produced in the atmosphere by reactions of other gases and vapors under the influence of the ultraviolet portion of solar radiation. It is one of the principal components of photochemical smog. Very small amounts of ozone (0.15–0.25 ppm) can damage the foliage of some plant species in a few hours of exposure. The injury appears as a fleck, bleach, or stipple of the upper surface of the oldest leaves. The type of symptom depends on the plant species. The extent of injury depends on the dosage, i.e., the concentration of ozone multiplied by duration of exposure. The symptoms appear on the foliage within about 24 hours after exposure, depending on weather conditions. Among the ozone-susceptible plants are tobacco, tomato, onion, pinto bean, cucumber, squash, and spinach. A resistant plant, easy to grow, is pepper.

Since gases usually enter the leaf through the stomata, ozone damage is greater when the stomata are fully opened. Conditions favoring such opening are (1) adequate water supply to the soil, (2) sufficient light on the plant, and (3) high relative humidity of the atmosphere.

IV. Equipment

1. Seeds of a susceptible species—bean, squash, or cucumber and pepper, a resistant species.
2. Trays and soil for germinating seeds.
3. Small pots for transplanting seedlings.
4. A large bell jar or a transparent plastic or glass chamber for exposing plants to ozone.
5. A lamp for generating ozone in a suitable opaque container. (Lamp—GE 4 S 11 and ballast —GE 89 G 381 or GE 89 G 504; available from an electrical supply house.)

V. Procedure

Seeds may be germinated in soil in aluminum trays, such as used for frozen foods. Transfer a dozen seedlings of each species to small pots and let them grow until they are about 8″ tall.

The ozone lamp will have to be wired in series with the ballast in 120-volt AC electric circuit so that proper lamp voltage will not be exceeded. The ballast develops considerable heat and should not be enclosed with the lamp. (If ballast is not available, a 100-watt incandescent lamp wired in series in the circuit makes a good substitute.)

Make a miniature fumigation chamber with glass or plastic or, if that is not possible, use the largest bell jar you have. Put the ozone bulb in a central position in the chamber and group the plants around it. Cover the fumigation chamber with heavy opaque cloth to protect your eyes or, better yet, pump the ozone/air mixture into the chamber from an exterior ozone generator such as described in Experiment No. 7. (To avoid eye injury, *never look at the lamp when lighted or at the ultraviolet radiation emanating from it.*) Remove the plants at intervals, put them back under normal growing conditions, and observe them for the next two days.

When a chamber 2′ × 2′ × 2′ was used, fumigation periods of 30, 60, and 90 minutes were sufficient to produce different degrees of ozone damage on the susceptible species. You should vary the time, depending on the size of your chamber.

Record the nature of the symptoms on each species, rate the relative susceptibility of each species, and determine the effect of dosage on plant response.

If proper equipment is available, the plant tissue may be examined microscopically.

If this experiment has been combined with Experiment No. 3, you will be able to compare the effect of ozone on living plants with that produced on a non-living material.

VI. References

1. Daines, R. H., Ida A. Leone, and Eileen Brennan, Air Pollution As It Affects Agriculture in New Jersey. N.J. Agr. Expt. Sta. Bull. 794, 14 pp; 1960.

2. Treshow, Michael, Environment and Plant Response, Chapter 18: 322–350; McGraw Hill Book Co., 1970.

3. Recognition of Air Pollution Injury to Vegetation: A Pictorial Atlas. Informative Report No. 1, TR-7 Agricultural Committee, Air Pollution Control Association, 1970.

VII. Prepared by Eileen Brennan and Ida Leone

EXPERIMENT NO. 7

Effect of Sulfur Dioxide and Ozone on Vegetation

I. Object

1. To demonstrate injury to leaves of vegetation following fumigation with low concentrations of sulfur dioxide and ozone gases in air.
2. To teach identification of typical leaf damage due to absorption of sulfur dioxide or ozone.
3. To teach techniques of fumigating vegetation.

II. Suitability and Usefulness

1. Can be used as a demonstration project to indicate potential economic losses to farmers and growers of ornamental shrubs and flowers within the school district.
2. Develops a sense of the relationship between air pollution and botany in the minds of students.
3. Teaches techniques of fumigating vegetation and identifying the cause of injury.
4. Would be particularly suited to advanced study of vegetation injury. (The experiment is a relatively costly one. This should be considered before purchasing compressed gases, pumps, flowmeters, etc.)

III. Theory

Sulfur dioxide (SO_2) and ozone (O_3) are among the most widespread of the gaseous air contaminants. Sulfur dioxide is produced by combustion of fossil fuels and processing of sulfur-containing materials. Ozone is a secondary air pollutant and one reaction by which it is produced naturally is the action of the ultraviolet portion of solar radiation on oxides of nitrogen:

$$NO_2 + h\nu \rightarrow NO + O$$

$$O + O_2 \rightarrow O_3$$

Note: The term $h\nu$ represents one photon of ultraviolet radiation which strikes one molecule of NO_2 and excites it with subsequent dissociation into NO and O.

The ozone produced in the atmosphere may participate in a number of other chemical and photochemical reactions.

Both sulfur dioxide and ozone produce characteristic symptoms on the leaves of susceptible plants. These are described in some detail in Experiment No. 8. It should be pointed out that acute exposure of susceptible plants to relatively high concentrations of sulfur dioxide (1–2 ppm) or ozone (0.5–1 ppm) will result in leaf injury in an hour or less. Chronic exposures at lower concentrations of sulfur dioxide (0.2–0.5 ppm) or ozone (0.05–0.10 ppm) for longer time periods (from one day to many days, depending on the plant species selected) will produce chlorosis (yellowing) or premature senescence (aging) of leaves.

Some plants are more susceptible to injury by sulfur dioxide or ozone than others. A few of the more susceptible species common to the eastern United States are: alfalfa, barley, tomato, carrot, lettuce, bean, table beet, zinnia, morning glory, violet, white pine and Norway maple. Ragweed is also highly susceptible, and students may wish to

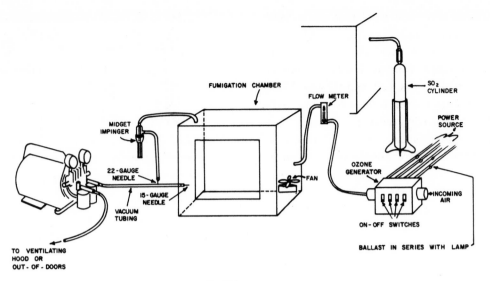

Fig. 7-1

APPARATUS FOR FUMIGATION OF PLANTS AND SAMPLING OF AIR

determine whether sulfur dioxide injury affects the pollen production of this troublesome native plant. The relative susceptibilities of a number of plant species to ozone and sulfur dioxide are given in Experiment No. 8.

The primary factor controlling gas absorption by the leaves is the degree of opening of the stomata. Absorption is at its maximum when the stomata are fully open, and vice versa. Most plants regularly close their stomata at night; hence, they are much more resistant to sulfur dioxide or ozone at night than during the day. Light, adequate moisture supply for the roots, high relative humidity, and moderate temperature are the conditions most conducive to opening of the stomata. Alfalfa is one plant which does not close its stomata at night; thus, it is subject to sulfur dioxide injury both day and night.

IV. Equipment

1. Seed or seedlings of the plants selected for study.
2. Flats, pots, and good garden soil for starting seed and growing seedlings.
3. Two small fumigation chambers of light wood or metal frame structure covered with Mylar plastic sheet (see Fig. 7-1). Boxes should be reasonably airtight. (*Note:* Cost can be minimized by reducing the size of the fumigation chambers.)
4. SO_2 gas cylinder, containing approximately 10 parts per million of sulfur dioxide in air. The gaseous mixture will be under pressure in the cylinder. A pressure reducing valve, obtainable from the gas supplier, should be secured for releasing the gas from the cylinder. Source of gas and valve—The Matheson Company, East Rutherford, N.J., Scott Research Laboratories, Inc.,

Plumsteadville, Pa., or other reputable gas suppliers. (*Note:* Sulfur dioxide concentration may decrease if allowed to remain in cylinders over long periods of time. Thus, the smallest available cylinder, consistent with the amount of gas needed, should be purchased.)
5. An ozone generator consisting of four G.E. 4-S-11 ozone-generating lamps, four sockets, and four G.E. 89-G-504 ballasts. Mount lamps in wood, aluminum or opaque plastic box or cylinder, airtight except for an inlet and outlet port. (Each ballast must be wired in series with its lamp. If the specified ballast is not available, a 100-watt incandescent lamp makes a suitable ballast. All ballasts should be mounted outside of the lamp box because they generate considerable heat in operation.) Each ozone lamp should be controlled by a separate switch so that different concentrations of ozone can be generated (see Fig. 7-1). When air is passed over the lamps, some of the oxygen of the air will be converted to ozone. (*To avoid eye injury, never look at the lamp when lighted or at the ultraviolet radiation it produces. Cover of box should be closed before lamps are lighted.*)
6. A suitable vacuum pump (such as Gast 1 VAF-10-M 100X, Gast Manufacturing Co., Benton Harbor, Michigan).
7. Suitable lengths of plastic (Teflon) or glass tubing.

Note: Use of the particular plastics specified in 3 and 7 is essential to prevent sorption of sulfur dioxide or ozone by the plastic.

8. Small motor-driven fan to circulate the gas/air mixture in the fumigation chamber.

9. A flow meter with a regulating valve, range 2.0–20 standard cubic feet per hour (SCFH). One SCFH is equal to 0.47 liters per minute (LPM). Thus, the flow meter will have a range of approximately 1 to 10 LPM. (One type is Dwyer Model RMA-BV-6 from Dwyer Instruments, Inc., P.O. Box 373, Michigan City, Indiana 46360.)

10. Midget impingers for collecting samples of O_3 or SO_2. (These can be obtained from Gelman Instrument Co., Ann Arbor, Mich. (Cat. No. 7202), or other suppliers.)

11. Rubber vacuum hose, $\frac{3}{16}$-inch inside diameter, about 2 feet.

12. Standard rubber hose, $\frac{1}{4}$-inch inside diameter, about 2 feet.

13. 22-Gauge hypodermic needles, 1-inch long.

14. 15-Gauge hypodermic needles, 1-inch long.

15. Copper wire (#18 rubber-covered lamp cord and electrical fittings).

16. Stopwatch with sweep second hand.

V. Reagents*

A. For Sulfur Dioxide

1. 0.01 N Sulfuric Acid—*Slowly* pour 3 ml. of concentrated sulfuric acid (specific gravity, 1.84) into 50 ml. of water. (*Be careful! Never add the water to the acid.*) Allow the solution to cool, then dilute to 1 liter in a volumetric flask. Take 100 ml. of this solution and dilute to 1 liter to make the final 0.01 N sulfuric acid solution.

2. 0.01 N Iodine Solution—Carefully weigh 1.269 grams of resublimed iodine crystals and 1.5 grams of potassium iodide (KI). Mix the KI with 2.5 ml. of water and transfer to a mortar with the previously weighed iodine crystals. Grind thoroughly with the pestle until all iodine is dissolved. Transfer with water to a volumetric flask and dilute to 1 liter. The solution should be stored in an amber bottle and refrigerated.

3. Starch Solution—Dissolve 1 gram of soluble starch in 500 ml. of cold water. Boil for a few minutes. Allow to cool and transfer to a 1 liter volumetric flask.

    a. Starch-Iodine-KI Solution—To the flask, add 2 ml. of 0.01 N sulfuric acid, 8 ml. of 0.01 N iodine solution, and 2 grams of KI. Dilute to 1 liter with water and store in a dark bottle or in a dark place.

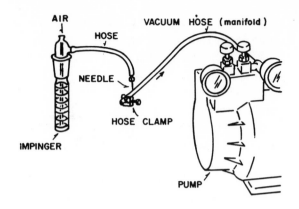

Fig. 7-2

CONNECTION OF AIR SAMPLER TO VACUUM PUMP

B. For Ozone

1. Starch—KI Solution—Dissolve 20 grams of KI in 50 ml. of starch solution prepared as in 3 above. Dilute with water to 1 liter and store in a dark bottle or in a dark place.

2. 0.005 N Sodium Thiosulfate—Weigh out 1.241 grams of sodium thiosulfate ($Na_2S_2O_3 \cdot 5H_2O$), transfer to a volumetric flask, dissolve with water, and dilute to 1 liter. (The solution then contains 0.79 g of $Na_2S_2O_3$, without water of crystalization, per liter.) This solution must be made fresh every 3 or 4 days.

VI. Procedure

Start the seeds in the flats and later transplant the seedlings to individual pots. Transfer the potted plants to the fumigation chambers. The chambers should be located and properly anchored on a level surface indoors or, if on the roof of the school, in a safely accessible place. If the fumigations are to be performed indoors, be sure that the chambers are well-sealed to prevent leakage into the room. Gases leaving the chamber should be exhausted, through the vacuum pump, out-of-doors or into a chemical ventilating hood. Plants fumigated indoors will also probably require supplementary light to ensure opening of stomata. This can be provided with high-intensity fluorescent lamps. When the plants have attained the desired size, the fumigation experiments may proceed.

* The Methods for the sampling and analysis of SO_2 and O_3 have been reprinted from *Chemistry* with permission of © American Chemical Society.

Set up chambers with plants inside and make connections as shown in Fig. 7-1.

Turn on vacuum pump and withdraw air from the chambers at a rate of about 14 liters per minute. This will be controlled by the 15-gauge hypodermic needle attached to the vacuum pump. Measure airflow with the flowmeter and begin injection of the pollutant into one chamber, SO_2 from the tank or ozone from the ozone-generating bulbs. The other chamber will serve as a control. The experimenter may wish to determine the effect of both pollutants together since they have been reported to have a synergistic effect. After the pollutant injection has started, connect the air sampler as shown in Fig. 7-2. The procedures for SO_2 and O_3 collection and analysis are as follows:

Sulfur Dioxide

Place 10 ml. of the starch-iodine-KI solution in the midget impinger. Push the 22-gauge hypodermic needle through the wall of the vacuum tubing so that it is in the internal bore of the tubing. Start the stopwatch. Air containing SO_2 is now withdrawn at 1 liter per minute, because of the limiting properties of the 22-gage needle, and is bubbled into the reagent solution. When the solution is completely decolorized, stop the stopwatch and withdraw the needle. Record the time of sampling to the nearest 0.1 minute.

Calculations

When a 22-gage, 1-inch long hypodermic needle is used, air passes through the liquid at a rate of 1 liter per minute. Therefore, the number of minutes the sample is run equals the number of liters of air passed through the solution. If 10 ml. of this solution were completely decolorized by the sulfur dioxide contained in 9.6 liters of air at 20°C., the concentration of SO_2 would be 1 ppm by volume.

This relationship can be computed as follows: Because 8 ml. of 0.01 N I_2 solution were diluted to 1 liter, the resulting solution is 8×10^{-5} N. One liter of a Normal solution of iodine contains 1 gram-equivalent of iodine and one ml. contains 1×10^{-3} gram-equivalent. Therefore, 1 ml. of 8×10^{-5} N iodine will contain 8×10^{-8} gram-equivalent. Ten milliliters of this solution were taken for sampling. Hence, 8×10^{-7} equivalent of I_2 was taken and will react with 8×10^{-7} equivalent of SO_2, according to the equation $SO_2 + I_2 + 2H_2O = 2HI + H_2SO_4$. Because there are two

gram-equivalents of SO_2 per mole, this is 4×10^{-7} mole. At 20°C. and 760 mm Hg, one gram-mole of gas occupies about 24 liters. Then 4×10^{-7} mole of gas occupies 9.6×10^{-6} liter, the volume occupied by enough pure SO_2 to react with 10 ml. of reagent. If this is mixed with 9.6 liters of air, the concentration is 1 ppm by volume. The same concentration will result if the computation is done by the method described in Experiment No. 22, "Analysis of SO_2 in Combustion Gases (Iodometric Method)." Students should become familiar with both methods.

Other concentrations can be computed, too, when it is known that the concentration of SO_2 is inversely proportional to the sampling time—that is, to the air volume sampled. This is so because the quantity of iodine is fixed at 10 ml. of 8×10^{-5} N solution. For example, if 48 liters of air caused complete decoloring of 10 ml. of reagent, then $9.6/x = 48/1$, or $x = 0.2$ ppm.

Ozone

Place 10 ml. of the starch-KI solution into the midget impinger. Add 1 ml. of 0.005 N sodium thiosulfate solution. Connect the impinger to the pump as described for SO_2. Start the stopwatch and note the time at the first indication of blue color in the solution. Stop the watch, withdraw the needle, and record the duration of sampling to the nearest 0.1 minute.

Calculations

Ozone reacted with the KI in the starch-iodide solution to form free iodine, which in turn reacted with the sodium thiosulfate to form sodium iodide, according to the following equations for volumetric analysis which you will find in many chemistry handbooks:

$$O_3 + 2KI + H_2O = O_2 + I_2 + 2KOH \quad (1)$$

$$2Na_2S_2O_3 + I_2 = 2NaI + Na_2S_4O_6 \quad (2)$$

By combining these equations, we see that one molecule of O_3 and two molecules of $Na_2S_2O_3$ took part in these reactions (with one molecule of iodine produced and consumed), or we can say that 316 mg. of $Na_2S_2O_3$ are equivalent to 48 mg. of O_3 (from molecular weights).

The 1 ml. of 0.005 N $Na_2S_2O_3$ used contained 0.79 mg. of $Na_2S_2O_3$. Then the weight of ozone equivalent to 1 ml. of 0.005 N $Na_2S_2O_3$

solution can be found from the following simple proportion:

$$x \text{ mg. } O_3 : 0.79 \text{ mg. } Na_2S_2O_3 = 48 : 316$$

$$x = 0.79 \times \frac{48}{316} = 0.12 \text{ mg., or } 12 \times 10^{-5} \text{ gram of } O_3.$$

Since the molecular weight of ozone in grams at 20°C and 760 mm Hg occupies about 24 liters, we can compute the corresponding volume of ozone as follows:

$$12 \times 10^{-5} \times \frac{24}{48} = 6 \times 10^{-5} \text{ liter}$$

If air was drawn through the reagent for 2 hours at 1 liter per minute before blue color was observed, total volume of air sampled was 120 liters. Then, the concentration of ozone in the air was

$$\frac{6 \times 10^{-5}}{120} \times 10^6 = \frac{10}{20} = 0.5 \text{ ppm by volume}$$

which is a concentration typical of a severe, eye-irritating smog.

Since foliar symptoms of SO_2 or O_3 injury often require a considerable amount of time to develop, it may be necessary to delay observations for 1 or 2 days after the fumigation. Plants should be kept well-watered and exposed to an adequate amount of light for symptom development.

VII. Records

Keep careful notes of the experiments and descriptions of the symptoms. Take color photographs wherever possible for a permanent record.

VIII. Further Investigations

The student may wish to try other fumigation conditions, e.g., the amount of injury produced by fumigation in the dark vs. fumigation in the light; dark treatments before, during, or after fumigation; adequate vs. inadequate water; effect of different temperatures, etc.

IX. References

1. Wartburg, Arthur F. and James P. Lodge, Jr., Estimating concentration of air pollutants, Chemistry 41 (2): 29–32, 1968.
2. N. A. Lange, Handbook of Chemistry; Handbook Publishers, Inc., 1934.

X. Prepared by Leonard H. Weinstein and Jay S. Jacobson

EXPERIMENT NO. 8

Use of Native and Cultivated Plants to Evaluate the Effects of Air Pollution on Vegetation

I. Object

1. To evaluate the impact of air pollution to vegetation by the use of native weeds, commonly-grown ornamental plants, and vegetables or by using selected biological monitors.

II. Suitability and Usefulness

1. Can be the subject of a class or science club project or a term paper.
2. Useful in demonstrating relative susceptibilities of different plant species to air pollutants, in identifying common weeds and cultivated plants, and in identifying and distinguishing between foliar symptoms produced by different air pollutants and those produced by disease, insects, or physical factors.

3. Provides a valuable illustration of one of the possible ecological consequences of uncontrolled vehicular, power plant, and industrial pollution.

III. Theory

Since certain species of weeds are often widely distributed throughout any geographical area, they can serve as indicators for evaluating the impact of air pollution on the vegetation of that area. In addition to native weed species, many commonly cultivated annual and perennial ornamental plants and vegetables may also be valuable as indicators. In some areas a particular pollutant may be suspected but leaf symptoms are not distinctive because there are no suitable native or cultivated plant species susceptible to that pollutant. In this circumstance, a bioassay technique can be used and selected plant species or varieties known to be susceptible to different pollutants can be situated in field plots to aid in supplying the desired information. The proximity of injured vegetation to a known pollution source will make identification more accurate. Some pollutants may produce symptoms which are more specific and which can be identified with a reasonable degree of reliability.

There are three major groups of pollutants which affect vegetation in North America. These are photochemical oxidants, sulfur oxides and fluorides. Oxidants are produced in the atmosphere when vehicular and similar emissions are irradiated with ultraviolet light. A major component of photochemical smog is ozone. Peroxyacyl nitrate (PAN) and other oxidizing substances are also produced. Sulfur dioxide (SO_2) is a product of the combustion of fossil fuels, such as coal and oil, and of the smelting of metallic sulfide ores. Hydrogen fluoride (HF) and silicon tetrafluoride (SiF_4) are byproducts of primary aluminum smelting, phosphate fertilizer manufacture, and the brick, ceramic, and glass industries.

A description of the symptoms produced on plants by several important air pollutants is given below. The symptoms apply to plants in general, except where a certain plant species has been emphasized, and may vary somewhat between different genera or species as well as local growing conditions.

OZONE—Four types of ozone-induced markings have been distinguished on leaves of exposed plants: stipple, fleck, necrotic (dead) patches, and chlorosis (yellowing). The occurrence of each pattern depends upon the plant species, the concentration of ozone, duration of exposure, and the age of the leaf. It is not unusual to find two or more of these symptoms on a single plant.

Stipple consists of dark punctate markings (dots or very small spots) on the upper surface of the leaf caused by thickening and pigmentation in the walls of groups of underlying cells.

Flecking consists of light-colored lesions, larger than those described for stipple, scattered over the upper leaf surface. This symptom is caused by collapse and bleaching of underlying cells in the affected area.

Necrotic patches vary upwards in size from 1 mm.

in diameter and may include the entire leaf blade, although the patches usually occur between the leaf veins. *Necrotic patches* are bifacial, that is the lesion extends through the entire leaf. All cells in the injured area are collapsed. The color of the necrotic area ranges from ivory to light tan, and may occasionally be reddish.

Chlorosis and *premature senescence* (aging) of older leaves are also commonly occurring symptoms.

On leaves of grasses, ozone produces a fine chlorotic *strippling* between the veins. Under severe conditions, these chlorotic areas expand and coalesce to produce streaks between the veins. When necrosis appears, it is usually ivory to light tan in color and occurs as longitudinal streaks or is concentrated at the *arch* of the leaf. (As a grass leaf grows it tends to droop downward in response to gravity. The apex of this leaf curvature is the *arch*.)

In the maturing plant, older leaves are usually most susceptible. The youngest leaves are most resistant to injury. As the leaves expand, they become susceptible to ozone injury at the tips, and with continued expansion, more of the leaf becomes susceptible.

On needles of many pine trees, ozone symptoms appear as a yellow mottling toward the needle tip in new emerging or fully-expanded needles. This mottling continues toward the base as the needle tissues mature. As the condition becomes more severe, the mottled areas may become necrotic, age prematurely, and drop.

PEROXYACYL NITRATE (PAN)—Injury from PAN consists of glazing or bronzing on the undersurface of the leaf. In some species there is an initial bleaching of the undersurface of the leaf which often develops into light-tan necrotic areas. The glazed appearance is due to collapse of underlying cells with subsequent formation of air pockets between the collapsed cells and the lower epidermis. Acute exposure to PAN results in bifacial scorching of leaves and the appearance of necrotic spots with glazed margins.

SULFUR DIOXIDE—Initial symptoms of acute sulfur dioxide injury are often characterized by water-soaked or collapsed areas which are generally, but not always, confined to the leaf surfaces between the veins. The injured areas are bifacial and become sharply defined and dried within 24 hours after exposure, and within 48 hours become tan or buff colored. Leaves of broad-leaved plants generally show spotted marking between the veins, while leaves of narrow-leaved plants usually show necrotic streaks between the parallel veins on either side of the midvein, although injury may also appear along the leaf margins and tips. Under circumstances of very acute exposure, entire leaves may die and drop off. Conifer needles (such as pine) become brown and necrotic at the tips, and the transitional area between injured and uninjured tissue is generally chlorotic. Chronic (long-term, low concentrations) exposure to sulfur dioxide may result in yellowing of the leaf between the veins.

Middle-aged leaves are most susceptible to injury by sulfur dioxide.

HYDROGEN FLUORIDE (HF) OR SILICON TETRAFLUORIDE (SiF_4)—On most narrowed-leaved plants, the initial symptom of HF injury is yellowing of the leaf tips and margins of rapidly growing leaves, usually becoming necrotic. The color of the necrotic areas ranges from ivory or light tan through various shades of brown. On grasses, the initial symptom is the appearance of scattered chlorotic flecks at the tips and upper margins of expanding and recently-expanded leaves. The flecking may extend downward from the tip and along the leaf margins as the symptoms progress. The amount of chlorosis diminishes downward from the leaf tip and from the margins toward the midvein. At high HF concentrations, there is a greater tendency for tip, marginal, and interveinal necrosis. Pine needles become reddish-brown at the tips, and depending on the severity of the exposure, the injury may extend downward toward the base of the needles. The necrotic areas are often accompanied by narrow dark bands, each of which may represent the limits of separate exposures.

On broad-leaved plants, the initial symptoms are usually chlorosis of the tips and margins of expanding or recently-expanded leaves. In time, the chlorosis may extend to the areas between the leaf veins. With continued exposure, the leaf tips may become necrotic and fall off, leaving the leaf notched. Longitudinal expansion of the leaf may be inhibited resulting in a puckered or cupped appearance. At higher exposures, chlorotic areas of the leaf may become necrotic. These necrotic areas often fall from the leaf giving it a tattered appearance.

IV. Limitations

1. Plants can be used as indicators of pollution only during the spring and summer months since leaves are the organs exhibiting characteristic symptoms.

2. The student should be warned that the presence of a particular symptom on a plant under field conditions does not necessarily prove that the symptom was air pollution-induced. Symptoms produced by some pollutants are not always distinctive, and may resemble those induced by other environmental stresses, including drought, over-watering, extremes of temperature, under-or over-fertilization, insects, diseases, pesticides, or salt injury.

3. Areas near specific sources of air pollution provide the best opportunity for detecting injury to vegetation. In addition, large sections of the country are exposed to photochemical pollutants (such as ozone) derived from the action of solar radiation on motor vehicle exhaust gases. However, variation in symptom expression between species, the influence of growing conditions, and possible confusion of symptoms with those induced by disease, insects, or other factors, require careful observation and consideration of all possibilities by students.

V. Equipment and Supplies

1. Seeds or plants of special indicator species (e.g., alfalfa or squash for SO_2; tobacco for ozone; white-flowered petunia for PAN; gladiolus for fluoride) if special plots are to be installed. Accurate diagnosis of air pollution injury on plants requires that the student be able to identify receptor plants to both the genus and species. Suitable reference books which will assist in the identification of trees, shrubs, flowers, and weeds and to provide a close acquaintance with air pollution symptoms on plant leaves are available (see references).

2. Clay or plastic pots if needed.

3. 5-10-5 fertilizer.

VI. Procedure

A. Field surveys

An area suspected of severe air pollution during the spring, summer, or fall should be selected for surveillance. Careful observations should be made of plants, particularly those known to be susceptible to the suspected pollutants. Best observations are made in the late spring or early summer when

Relative susceptibilities of native and cultivated plants to sulfur dioxide, ozone, peroxyacetyl nitrate, and hydrogen fluoride

Common Name	Latin Name	SO_2	O_3	PAN	HF
Native Plants					
Eastern White Pine* (young needles)	Pinus strobus	MR	S		S
Eastern White Pine (mature needles)	Pinus strobus	S			R
Scrub Pine	Pinus virginiana		S		R
Jack Pine	Pinus banksiana		S		MR
Ponderosa Pine	Pinus ponderosa	S	S		S
Douglas Fir	Pseudotsuga menziesii		R		S
Blue Spruce	Picea pungens				MR
Hemlock	Tsuga canadensis		S		R
Pin Oak	Quercus palustris	R	S		R
Scarlet Oak	Quercus coccinea	R	S		R
Tulip Poplar	Liriodendron tulipifera		S	S	R
Norway Maple	Acer Platanoides	S	R	R	R
Prickly Lettuce	Lactuca serriola	S	S	S	R
Ragweed	Ambrosia artemisiifolia	S	R	R	MR
Chickweed	Stellaria media	S	S	S	S
Eastern Smartweed	Polygonum Persicaria	S	S		S
Horseweed	Erigeron annuus	S	R	R	MR
Narrow-Leaved Plantain	Plantago Lanceolata	S	R	R	R
Oxalis	Oxalis stricta	S	R	R	MR
Violet	Viola Sp.	S	R	MR	R
Orchard Grass	Dactylus glomerata	S	S	S	MR
Annual Bluegrass	Poa annua		S	S	MR
Cultivated Plants					
European Larch	Larix decidua	MR	S		S
European White Birch	Petula alba	MR	R	R	R
Box Elder	Acer Negundo	R	S	R	S
Alfalfa	Medicago sativa	S	S	MR	R
Pinto Bean	Phaseolus vulgaris	S	S	S	R
Tobacco	Nicotiana tabacum	S	S	MR	R
Cotton	Gossypium hirsutum	S	R	R	R
Barley	Hordeum vulgare	S	S	MR	MR
Beet	Beta vulgaris	S	R	S	R
Spinach	Spinacia oleracea	S	S	S	R
Cucumber	Cucumis sativus	R	MR	R	R
Sweet Corn	Zea mays	R	S	R	S
Tomato	Lycopersicon esculentum	S	S	MR	MR
Broccoli	Brassica oleracea italica	S	S	R	R
Squash	Cucurbita pepo	S	MR	R	R
Lettuce	Lactuca sativa	S	R	S	R
Carrot	Daucus carota	S	MR	R	R
Gladiolus	Gladiolus hortulanus	MR	R	R	S
Zinnia	Zinnia elegans	S	R	MR	R
Morning Glory	Ipomoea hederacea	S	R	R	R
Petunia	Petunia hybrida		S	S	R
Blueberry	Vaccinium corymbosum				S
Apricot	Prunus armeniaca	MR		R	S

*Younger needles of conifers are more susceptible to HF than older needles, while the reverse is generally true for SO_2.
S = Susceptible; MR = Moderately resistant; R = Resistant.

leaves are growing rapidly and before plants become senescent. Adverse conditions such as excess rainfall, drought, cold, heat, insect pests or diseases should be considered when making tentative explanations for symptoms.

If an initial survey indicates air pollution injury, other susceptible and resistant species should be observed. Patterns of injury relating to location of pollution sources and prevailing wind direction should be detectable. An attempt should be made to determine whether symptoms appear shortly after periods of stagnant weather or atmospheric inversion. If evidence accumulates indicating pollutant injury, plant indicator plots can be established to provide confirmatory evidence.

B. Indicator plants

Choose a susceptible and, if possible, a resistant species that will grow well in the region. Plant, fertilize, and water so that vigorous, disease-free plants are obtained. Wherever possible, locate plots near to and far from the polluted area. If potted plants are used, plants may be transferred from a clean to a polluted area after the plants have at least several mature leaves. Carefully observe the initial and later stages and refer to articles describing the symptoms caused by pollutants. The age of leaves and parts of leaves affected, and the size and color of lesions can aid in identifying the cause of injury.

VII. Records

When making field observations, the student should take careful notes describing his observations, the species of plants exhibiting symptoms, and those that do not. The exact location where the observations are made is important in determining the extent of plant injury and possibly relating it to a source. A road map is useful for this purpose. Color photographs are less subjective than word descriptions and should be made wherever possible to provide a permanent record.

VIII. References

1. Zim, H. S., Trees of North America; Golden Press, New York.
2. Zim, H. S., Wild Flowers of North America; Golden Press, New York.
3. Montgomery, F. H., and C. M. Switzer, Ontario Weeds; Publication 505, Ontario Department of Agriculture, Toronto, Ontario.
4. Jacobson, J. S., and A. C. Hill, Editors. Recognition of Air Pollution Injury to Vegetation: A Pictorial Atlas. Informative Report No. 1, TR-7 Agricultural Committee, Air Pollution Control Association, 4400 Fifth Ave., Pittsburgh, Pa. 15213; 1970.
5. Hindawi, I. J., Air pollution injury to vegetation; National Air Pollution Control Administration Publication No. AP-71, 1970. (Available from Superintendent of Documents, U.S. Government Printing Office, Washington, D.C. 20402 at $1.25 per copy.)

IX. Prepared by Leonard H. Weinstein and Jay S. Jacobson

EXPERIMENT NO. 9

Effect of Soil Nutrition on Injury to Vegetation by Gaseous Air Pollutants

I. Object

1. To determine whether susceptible species of plants grown in a nutritionally balanced soil are more resistant to air pollution injury than plants of the same species grown in soil deficient in organic matter and mineral nutrients.

II. Suitability and Usefulness

1. Gives students an opportunity to experiment in a field in which there seems to have been little investigation to date.

2. Provides an opportunity to relate air pollution to agronomy in their effects on plant health.

III. Background

Before his untimely death, Louis Bromfield wrote four excellent books on his experiences, over a period of about twenty years, in the restoration of several worn-out farms in north central Ohio. They are, in order of publication, Pleasant Valley, Malabar Farm, Out of the Earth, and From My Experience. They are recommended reading for everyone interested in ecology, the environment, and the controversy over the future means of feeding our burgeoning population.

One of his observations, repeated many times, is that plants grown in nutritionally balanced soil resist disease and insect attacks. If this is true, are plants grown in nutritionally balanced soil also more resistant to injury by gaseous air pollutants in the concentrations usually found in the atmosphere?

Unfortunately, we do not know exactly what the composition of a nutritionally balanced soil should be. But we do know that it should contain an abundance of organic matter in the form of rotted barnyard manure and decayed garden trash plus peat moss for moisture retention and lightening of the soil. When broken down by soil organisms, this organic matter becomes humus which is so essential to the transformation of soil minerals to forms readily useable for plant growth. The soil should also contain mineral nutrients, such as nitrogen, phosphorus, potassium, calcium, magnesium and sulfur in fair abundance plus many other elements in only trace amounts. In addition, there should be present a working population of earthworms and other beneficial organisms usually found in a healthy soil.

IV. Equipment

1. Exposure chambers, the same or similar to those described in Experiment No. 7.

2. Cylinder of compressed SO_2 in air—concentration about 10 ppm. Also a pressure reducing valve for the cylinder. Both are available from reputable suppliers, such as The Matheson Company, East Rutherford, New Jersey or Scott Research Laboratories, Inc., Plumsteadville, Pa.

3. Flats or pots of sufficient size to accommodate the plants selected for study (8 are needed).

V. Materials

1. Loam, so nutritionally depleted that only a few scraggly weeds grow naturally on it.

2. Loam, as nutritionally complete or balanced, as it is possible to make it. (See VI, Procedure.)

3. Rotted manure (cow or sheep), garden trash (weeds, sod, roots, leaves, etc.) or compost, vegetable food scraps, and peat moss for supply of organic matter.

4. Hydrated lime, $Ca(OH)_2$, to adjust pH of soil.

5. *Complete* commercial fertilizer to supply proper amounts of nitrogen, phosphorus, and potassium, as well as trace amounts of B, Mn, Zn, Mo, Fe, Cu, etc.

6. Commercial 5-10-5 fertilizer.

7. Seeds of the susceptible plants selected for study: bean, cucumber, squash, radish, corn, barley, etc.

VI. Procedure

A. Preparation of soil

1. Select two adjacent 6′ × 6′ plots where the soil is nutritionally depleted, as described above.

2. In mid-September, turn over an 8-inch depth of the soil in place or bring the soil from each plot to convenient outdoor sites at the school.

3. Plot I soil should be raked fairly level, but otherwise should be untreated.

4. To the soil of Plot II, add the types of organic matter listed to the extent of 50% of the volume of the soil. Spread about 10 lbs. of hydrated lime over the surface. Thoroughly mix soil, lime and organic matter. Rake the surface fairly level and seed it to winter rye. Rake again to cover the seed.

5. As soon as the soil can be worked in the spring, disc or cultivate the green rye into the soil of Plot II.

6. Divide the soil of each plot into two equal parts and designate them Plots Ia, Ib, IIa, and IIb.

7. To the soil of Plot Ia add 5-10-5* commercial fertilizer and to the soil of Plot IIa add a *complete* commercial garden fertilizer in amounts as recommended on the packages for an area of 18 sq. ft.

8. Thoroughly mix the soil in Plots Ia, Ib, IIa, and IIb.

B. Plant culture

1. Fill 2 pots with each of the 4 soils. Label each pot to indicate type of soil.

---

*The 5-10-5 fertilizer is used in Plot Ia because this is the type of commercial fertilizer more generally used in farming operations.

2. In each pot, sow the seeds of the type plant selected for growing. Cover the seeds and moisten the soil.

3. Thin the seedlings so that there will be plenty of room for full growth in each pot.

4. After all danger of frost is past, set the pots of plants outside where they will get plenty of sunlight and rain. Water them as necessary.

C. Plant fumigation—(when plants are of moderate size)

1. Examine plants for any leaf injury before fumigation. Photograph them if found.

2. Use the procedure described in Experiment No. 7 and fumigate the plants with sulfur dioxide as described.

3. Remove the plants from the fumigation chamber and observe them carefully for development of visible leaf injury resulting from fumigation, noting any significant differences between plants grown in soils Ia, Ib, IIa, and IIb.

Note: If all plants should be injured, would using lower concentrations of SO_2 or a shorter period of fumigation be of any benefit?

VII. Evaluation

1. Estimate any differences in the amount of leaf injury found with the plants grown in each of the four types of soil. Measure affected leaf areas with a millimeter scale, and compute the approximate total leaf area damaged in relation to plant growth.

2. Note whether there are any differences in the nature or type of injury with respect to soil type. Observe injured leaf areas with a microscope if necessary.

3. Note any differences in plant growth and weight with respect to soil type.

4. If you found significant differences in the amount of injury with respect to soil type, what suggestions would you make to your parents and neighbors to avoid at least some of the effects of local air pollution?

5. If you should find that plants grown in nutritionally deficient soil are less resistant to air pollution injury than those grown in a healthy, nutritionally balanced soil, would you consider it any less of an ecological sin to permit nutritional depletion of the soil than it is to pollute the air?

VIII. Applicability

If no difference in the amount of injury can be found the first year, who wants to repeat the experiment a second and third year, treating the same plots of soil the same way each year on the possibility that nutritional balance will become better with time?

IX. References

1. N. Lacasse and W. Moroz, Handbook of Effects Assessment; The Pennsylvania State University, 1970.

2. Design of a Simple Plant Exposure Chamber; Department of Health, Education and Welfare, U.S. Public Health Service, Bulletin APTD-68-6.

3. Jay S. Jacobson and A. Clyde Hill, Editors, Recognition of Air Pollution Injury to Vegetation —A Pictorial Atlas; Informative Report No. 1, TR-7 Agricultural Committee, Air Pollution Control Association, 1970.

4. Louis Bromfield, (1) Pleasant Valley, (2) Malabar Farm, (3) Out of the Earth, (4) From My Experience; Harper and Brothers.

5. Barry Commoner, The Closing Circle; Alfred A. Knopf, Inc., 1971.

X. Prepared by Robert L. Marino and Donald C. Hunter

EXPERIMENT NO. 10

Emission Source Inventory

I. Object

1. To calculate the weight of pollutants discharged into the air of an urban community.

2. To examine and evaluate the weight of pollutants discharged into the air by public, institutional, and industrial sources of an urban community.

Table 1

Emission Inventory of Air Pollutants for the United States (million of tons per year)

Source	CO	Hydrocarbons	NO$_x$	SO$_2$	Particulates	Total by Source
Transportation	64.5	17.6	7.6	0.4	1.2	91.3
Fuel combustion, stationary sources	1.9	0.7	6.7	22.9	9.2	41.4
Industrial processes	10.7	3.5	0.2	7.2	7.6	29.2
Garbage incineration	7.6	1.5	0.5	0.1	1.0	10.7
Miscellaneous*	16.9	8.2	1.7	0.6	9.6	37.0
Total by Type	101.6	31.5	16.7	31.2	28.6	209.6

*Includes emissions from forest fires.

Source: NAPCA, 1966 data.

II. Suitability and Usefulness

1. Develops an understanding of the magnitude of pollutant emissions by category.

2. Serves to indicate where enforcement of air pollution should be emphasized.

3. May be used as a comparison of one community's air pollution problem with that of another community based upon the weight of emissions.

III. Theory

Air pollution reaches the atmosphere as emissions of particles, gases, vapors, and fumes from man's various activities. An inventory of these emissions is a major part of air resource management. The emission inventory of air pollutants investigates and documents all sources, evaluates the effectiveness of air pollution control devices, and presents the weight of specific pollutants released in an area on a time basis. It provides an important measure of the total pollution burden on the atmospheric resources of any given air basin or community. An updated emission inventory is a prerequisite for continued evaluation of air pollution problems in an area.

In addition to defining the weight of pollutants discharged by public, institutional, commercial, and industrial sources on a time basis, other specific uses of the emission inventory are:

    a. helps locate monitoring stations and alert networks,

    b. indicates seasonal and geographical distribution of the air pollution burden,

    c. assists in developing a control program and in determining priority problems,

    d. indicates air quality changes,

    e. provides a descriptive model of atmospheric dispersion,

    f. may be used for regional planning and zoning,

    g. can be used to educate a community and industry,

    h. may be used as a prediction of future air quality trends in a community, and

    i. may be used to unite the community in attacking air pollution problems.

The emission inventory may be compared to a parts or raw material inventory of a large corporation. For a smoothly running industrial organization, it is essential that a detailed accounting of the amounts of raw material is known for a regular time basis. So it is with the source emission inventory for a smoothly functioning air pollution control agency.

However, an urban community consists of a complex arrangement and number of public, commercial, institutional and industrial operations. These activities involve the use of such air-polluting sources as motor vehicles, buses, railroads, airplanes, rockets, home heating, refuse disposal, factories, mills, and power generating plants. Air pollution starts with the production of emissions—often as an undesirable or incidental consequence of these public, commercial, institutional, and industrial necessities. In many instances it becomes worse as the various particles, gases, and vapors become intimately mixed in the atmosphere where ultraviolet radiation from the sun starts a chain reaction of photochemical activity.

Despite the complexity of air pollution, it is possible to account for the amount of air pollutants discharged into the air of a given community. Such tabulations may be used as an objective measure of air pollution.

IV. Equipment

1. Pencil, paper, and slide rule.
2. Copies of reference material particularly references 1 and 5.

V. Procedure

Table 1 may be used for a rough estimate of the emission inventory for many of the larger cities by population ratio with that of the United States. In comparing the population in a community to the population of the United States in 1966, the yearly emission of the various pollutants listed in the table may be calculated directly. One example of such calculation is given below.

Assume: U.S. population   195 million
City population   1.5 million

Weight of sulfur dioxide (SO_2) discharged yearly from fuel combustion from stationary sources for the city is:

$$\frac{1.5 \times 10^6 \text{ (population)}}{195 \times 10^6 \text{ (population)}} \times 22.9 \times 10^6 \frac{\text{tons } SO_2}{\text{year}} = \frac{0.176 \text{ tons } SO_2}{\text{year}}$$

Obviously the calculation of air pollutant emissions by use of the above table is inaccurate, and would be grossly so for smaller communities with a few large sources. The accuracy of the emission inventory can be improved by obtaining factual data from a variety of sources for fuels consumed, vehicles registered, refuse burned, industrial employment, as well as other information useful to the emission survey. From such information, fuel usage for a specific category is calculated, the weight of emissions from fuel burning is then calculated, based on published factors for each type of fuel consumed. Details of the more exact procedure have been prepared by the Environmental Protection Agency. They are documented in references 1, 5, and 7; these references will be helpful in determining emissions from small communities. In using the emissions tables, you may find your community has an industry for which there is no table; in that event, you may want to personally interview the

plant superintendent for information from which you might estimate emissions.

VI. Records

A complete and neat record of each emissions inventory will enhance the work and increase its importance to you and the public. A bar chart, with each bar representing the estimated emission of each contaminant in pounds or tons per year, is suggested to illustrate your findings for greatest effectiveness.

VII. References

1. Ozolins, G., and Smith, R., "A Rapid Survey Technique for Estimating Community Air Pollution Emissions," U.S. Public Health Service Publication #999-AP-29, Cincinnati, Ohio, October 1966.
2. National Coal Association, Steam Electric Plant Factors, 1130 17th Street, N.W., Washington, D.C., 1965.
3. American Petroleum Institute, Petroleum Facts and Figures, 1271 Avenue of Americas, New York 20, N.Y., 1965.
4. Automobile Manufacturers Association, Motor Truck Facts and Automobile Facts and Figures, 320 New Center Building, Detroit, Mich. 48202, 1966.
5. Duprey, R. L., "Compilation of Air Pollutant Emissions Factors," U.S. Public Health Service Publication Number 999-AP-42, U.S. Department of Health, Education and Welfare, National Air Pollution Control Administration, Raleigh, N.C., 1968.
6. Wohlers, H. C., W. E. Jackson, and I. Gutmanis, "A Rapid Emission Survey Procedure for Industrial Air Pollutants," *Journal of Air Pollution Control Association* **19**, 309–314, 1969.
7. Compilation of Air Pollutant Emission Factors. Office of Air Programs Publication No. AP-42, Environmental Protection Agency, Research Triangle Park, N.C., February 1972.

VIII. Prepared by Henry C. Wohlers

EXPERIMENT NO. 11

Collection, Identification, and Counting of Ragweed Pollen

I. Object

1. To sample for ragweed pollen in the atmosphere.
2. To identify ragweed pollen under magnification.
3. To learn the proper techniques of counting magnified ragweed pollen.
4. To help the student relate the amount of ragweed pollen collected to respiratory irritation.

II. Suitability and Usefulness

1. Can be used as a qualitative experiment at the junior high school level, and as a quantitative determination at the senior high level in General Science and Biology classes.
2. Teaches the student techniques in microscopic identification.
3. Can be used to stimulate interest in field identification and nature of the ragweed plant.
4. Can develop the student's interest in public health and in means of controlling ragweed.
5. If desired, the experiment can be made a cooperative venture, with some students building the sampler, some preparing slides, some sampling for pollen, and others doing the counting.

III. Theory

Blossoming of ragweed is triggered by the lengthening nights of late July and early August. As blossoms of the ragweed plant mature, pollen is expelled by nature for the purpose of fertilizing seeds produced in the ovary of the blossom. Pollen release or expulsion is accomplished in the several hours after sunrise. Solar warming lowers the relative humidity of the air around the mature florets and, after the anthers or pollen sacs have dried sufficiently, they rupture. Because nature is grossly extravagant in production of fertilizing media, billions of pollen grains are caught up by the wind and remain airborne for varying distances, depending on their size and the nature and strength of air currents. Research has shown that the majority of ragweed pollen grains (about 95%) settle to the ground after being airborne for about 200 feet.

Ragweed pollen is perhaps the most trouble-some of all pollens and mold spores to those who are allergic. One survey in New York State indicated that approximately 10% to 15% of the population suffer from hayfever. Most of these people are allergic to ragweed pollen and suffer from hayfever from about August 15th to September 15th. The worst days are usually August 31st and September 1st when concentrations of ragweed pollen in the air are greatest.

Sampling is based on the fact that pollen grains can be caught and held on a suitable sticky surface. They can be examined and counted under magnification at a convenient time. A sampler devised by Dr. O. C. Durham of The American Academy of Allergy is the simplest and most widely used. However, its collection efficiency may be low and erratic.

IV. Equipment

1. Durham sampler (see Fig. 11-1); can be built by students in school shop.
2. Glass microscope slides (1″ × 3″) with one end frosted ¾″ on one side; Esco #2951 frosted, Erie Scientific, 693 Seneca St., Buffalo 10, N.Y., or equivalent.
3. Silicone stopcock grease; Dow Corning Corp., Midland, Mich., or equivalent.
4. Microscope, preferably with a mechanical stage, capable of 100× magnification.
5. Whipple disc for the eye-piece of the microscope. This is a small glass disc on which cross-section lines have been etched. It can be purchased for about $16.00 from laboratory supply houses such as Will Corporation, Rochester, N.Y.
6. Small hand counter, capacity 1 to 9,999; Cat. #4481, Will Corporation, Rochester, N.Y., or equivalent; cost approximately $11.00.
7. Slide boxes, slotted inside to hold 25 slides.
8. Window slide (described later).

V. Procedure

1. Placing the sampler
   a. Select a spot preferably on the roof of a two- or three-story building, well away from any superstructures which might affect free movement of the air near the sampler.

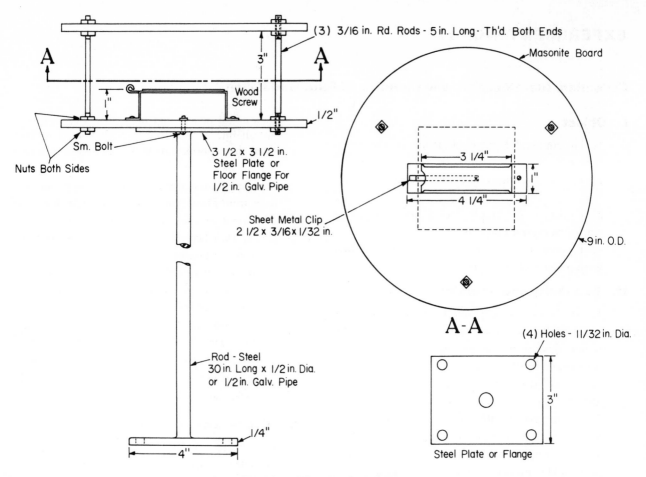

Fig. 11-1- POLLEN SAMPLER

b. Attach the lower end of the sampler stand to a 2′ × 2′ piece of plywood.

c. Place the sampler at the selected site, being sure the sampling head is at least 30 inches higher than any roof parapet. An empty steel drum makes a handy base for the sampler if it has to be raised.

d. Turn the sampler so that the long axis of the slide holder is parallel with prevailing wind direction. Weight the plywood base with a concrete block, or equivalent, to keep the sampler from blowing over.

2. Greasing the slides (at some convenient time before sampling is to begin)

a. Lay the first slide on a table or desk, frosted side up, and hold it between the thumb and forefinger of one hand.

b. Put a very small amount of silicone stopcock grease on the forefinger of the other hand.

c. Make several sweeps with the middle finger over the topside clear surface of the slide, leaving a very smooth and thin film of grease

on the glass. (The film of grease should be made as thin as possible.) Do not allow grease on the frosted portion.

d. Mark the frosted surface with an X to indicate the slide has been greased.

e. Place the greased slide in the first pair of slots in the slide box, *taking care not to touch or smear the greased surface.*

f. Proceed in like manner with as many other slides as are desired for the experiment. Then place the cover on the box to keep dust from reaching the greased slides before use.

3. Operating the Durham sampler

a. At, or near, 8:00 a.m. on the day sampling is to start, take the box of greased slides to the sampler site. Remove No. 1 slide from the box and enter the date with soft black pencil on the frosted portion of the slide. (Example: 9/7/68. The date of each sample is the date exposure *starts*, even though the slide will be exposed for 24 hours and, in this example, counted 9/8/68, or later.) Use care not to touch the greased surface. Replace the box cover immediately.

b. Hold the slide at its frosted end by thumb and finger of one hand.

c. Depress the spring clip of the slide holder with a finger of the other hand and push the slide into the slotted holder. (Be sure the frosted and greased side of the slide is *up*.)

d. Release the spring clip so it locks the slide in position.

e. Return the box and remaining slides to indoor storage space.

f. At the end of 24 hours, return to the sampling site with the box of slides, depress the spring clip on the sampler, remove the exposed slide from the holder, and return it to its position in the slide box, *being careful not to touch the greased surface.*

g. Remove a fresh slide (No. 2) from the box, enter the date on the frosted portion, and place it in the holder as before. Replace the cover on the box and return the box to indoor storage.

h. Repeat the operation each morning, exposing one slide each day.

4. Counting pollen

To obtain an indication of the amount of ragweed pollen present in the atmosphere, the grains of pollen in an area of two square centimeters on the exposed slide are counted under magnification. For counting, 100× magnification is usually used; this magnification can be realized with 10× Ocular and 10× Objective. But, for closer inspection of a particular grain, higher magnification, such as 10× Ocular and 40× Objective, is helpful.

When in focus with proper light at 100× magnification, the ragweed pollen grains have the appearance of small straw-colored golf balls.

To determine a 2 square centimeter area for counting, a window slide can be made by outlining an area 2.0 cm. × 1.0 cm. near the middle portion of a clean slide, the 2 cm. dimension being parallel to the long dimension of the slide. Gummed labels with straight, non-frayed edges may be used to make the 2 sq. cm. clear area permanent.

Identification and counting of ragweed pollen should proceed as follows:

a. Remove the exposed slide from the box and place it, exposed or greased side up, on top of the window slide, with the framed window up, on the microscope stage.

b. Focus *up* on the sample; that is, focus first on one of the lower planes of the pair of slides, and then raise the focus until the uppermost plane is being viewed. (It is often advisable for the beginner to use a slide with heavy collection of pollen as a help in learning proper focusing technique.)

c. Move the slides on the stage, either mechanically or by hand, so the greased slide over one corner of the window area is being viewed. (The microscope condenser may be lowered a little to regulate the illumination and sharpen the details of the pollen grains. Frequent manipulation of the fine adjustment should keep the individual pollen grains in sharp focus.)

d. Then traverse the slides so one east-west strip, the 2 cm. length of the window area, is being viewed. Use the hand counter to tally the number of ragweed pollen grains seen, without removing the eye from the microscope field. (The Whipple disc is helpful in breaking up the window area into an exact east-west, north-south grid.)

e. Move the slides mechanically or by hand so the next east-west strip can be viewed.

f. Then traverse the second strip as in step d, being sure a second count is not made of any pollen grains in the first strip.

g. Continue counting the pollen grains in east-west strips until the full 1 cm. width has been viewed.

h. Record the total number of pollen grains counted in the 2 sq. cm. area, divide by 2, and report the number of grains per sq. cm. of collecting surface as the count for the day. (The result will be either a whole number or a whole number plus a half.) Example:

Number of grains on 2 sq. cm.	Reported count per sq. cm.
8	4
6	3
9	4.5
7	3.5
14	7.0*

*This is the daily count at and above which those who are allergic are most apt to begin noticing hayfever symptoms.

i. Put a check mark on the frosted surface to indicate the slide has been counted.

Note to Teacher: You may wish to have several students count the same slide to demonstrate the concept of reproducibility of precision.

VI. References

1. Manual of Field Operating Practice; New York State Department of Health.

2. Experiences with the New York State Ragweed Pollen Sampling Program, D. C. Hunter and C. S. Maneri; Northeastern Weed Control Conference, January 1963.

3. Twenty-four-Hour Dispersion of Ragweed Pollen from Known Sources, G. S. Raynor and E. C. Ogden; Brookhaven National Laboratory, May 1966.

4. The Air Pollution Menace of Ragweed Pollen, Charles N. Howison; Northeastern Weed Control Conference, January 1967.

5. Journal of the Air Pollution Control Association, October 1967.

6. A Manual of Clinical Allergy, Saunders, Lovell, and Mathews; W. B. Saunders Co., 1953.

7. Pollen Grains, R. P. Wodehouse; McGraw-Hill, 1935.

8. Pollen Slide Studies, G. T. Brown; Charles G. Thomas, 1949.

VII. Prepared by Donald C. Hunter

EXPERIMENT NO. 12

Sampling for Airborne Microorganisms

I. Object

To indicate the approximate population density of microorganisms existing in the air.

II. Suitability and Usefulness

1. Suitable for small groups of students (2 to 4 per group).

2. The experiment demonstrates that bacteria and other microorganisms exist in the air we breathe.

3. The experiment demonstrates that certain diseases may be transmitted from person to person even though actual physical contact is not made.

4. Repeating the experiment at different locations or sampling the same location at different times may yield significantly different results. Possibilities are: sampling indoor air vs. outdoor air, or sampling a room normally occupied by people vs. the same room that has been empty overnight or over a weekend.

III. Theory

Throughout the centuries, man has sought causes for epidemics and widespread diseases. Hippocrates (about 400 B.C.) taught that "Airs, Waters and Places" influenced the health of populations. As time progressed, theories regarding infection of people by airborne organisms were verified. Pasteur in the early 1860's showed air to be populated with germs of fermentation and putrefaction.

Not until the last 50 years has man really appreciated the fact that infectious droplets and airborne particles are major causes of infectious disease. The microbial flora of air is transient and variable. Air is not a medium in which microorganisms can grow but rather a carrier of particulate matter, dust, and droplets which may be laden with microbes. Airborne microorganisms may be carried on dust particles; they may be in or exist as the nuclei of large droplets that remain suspended only briefly and; they may be present as the nuclei of smaller droplets from which liquid will evaporate leaving only the nuclei. (In microbiological terms, these nuclei are known as droplet nuclei.) Atmospheric conditions (such as humidity, sunlight and temperature), size of the particle bearing the microorganisms, and the nature of the microorganisms all govern the ultimate fate of airborne microorganisms. Now it is realized that the droplet nuclei have become one of the most important means of infection and spread of so-called contact or droplet infections.

The actual number of bacteria (one type of microorganism) in indoor air may vary from 1 to 1,000 per cubic foot. Infection of open wounds from air is possible, and infection of other sorts, particularly of respiratory diseases, may occur during coughing, sneezing, and talking. The bacteria may be carried to other persons or to food by air currents or they may settle and be incorporated in dust only to become airborne when disturbed by normal indoor activities.

IV. Equipment

1. Cell counter, such as Quebec Colony Counter, *advisable but not necessary;* available from American Optical Company, Scientific Instrument Division, Buffalo, New York at about $138. (The instrument has a built-in grid, on which the petri dish is placed, to aid in counting.)

2. Petri dishes
   a. Quebec Colony Counter available:
   Standard petri dishes, 100 mm diameter × 15 mm deep; glass or disposable pre-sterilized clear plastic. (The clear plastic petri dish is OPTILUX No. 1001, available from hospital or biological suppliers of Falcon Plastics, 1950 Williams Drive, Oxnard, California 93030.)
   b. Quebec Colony Counter *not* available:
   Use INTEGRID, Quebec Grid plastic petri dish No. 1010, having a grid etched in the bottom of the dish to aid in counting. (Source of supply is the same as for non-grid plastic dishes above.)

3. Prepared standard method agar, tryptone glucose yeast agar, (available already premeasured, premixed and diluted in sterilized capped tubes from distributors of Baltimore Biological Lab Products, such as Mohawk Hospital Equipment Co., 310–314 Broad Street, Utica, New York 13503. When ordering, use BBL catalog No. 21030 for 10 preparations at about $3.40 or No. 21031 for 100 preparations at about $26.65.)

4. Paper towels.

5. Biological incubator or a warm, dark area with a relatively constant 20°C temperature.

V. Procedure

1. Prepare standard method agar by first melting the required amount of agar medium quickly in a

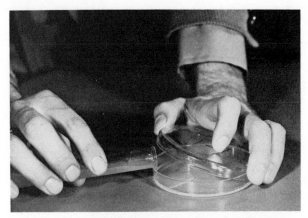
Fig. 12-1. Technique of pouring agar into petri dish.

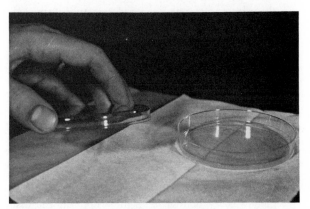
Fig. 12-2. Laying petri dish cover aside.

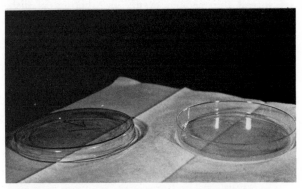
Fig. 12-3. Dish and cover during sampling period.

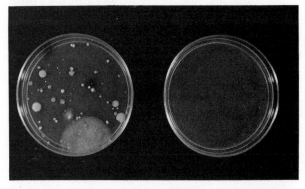
Fig. 12-4. Exposed and unexposed agar after incubation.

boiling water bath; approximately 10–20 minutes are required. When melting medium contained in prepared tubes with screw-on caps, loosen the cap slightly to allow for expansion during heating. Avoid prolonged exposure to unnecessarily high temperatures during and after melting. Melt one medium tube for each petri dish to be used. (If prepared medium is not used, see appendix for medium preparation.)

Cool the melted medium promptly to about 45°C (113°F) and hold at 44–46°C (111–115°F) in water bath or incubator until used.

2. Prepare sterilized petri dishes by introducing the contents of one prepared test tube (approximately 10–15 ml) of liquefied medium at 44–46°C into each dish by gently lifting the cover of the petri dish just high enough to pour the medium (Fig. 12-1). (Do not lift cover of dish completely off or agar may become contaminated by airborne bacteria and yield erroneous results.) When contents of tube are emptied into the dish, replace the cover until dish is scheduled for exposure. Avoid spilling any medium on outside of container or on inside of dish lid when pouring. Medium should completely cover bottom of dish; if not, tilt the dish slightly until desired coverage is achieved. Having spread the medium evenly over bottom of dish, let it solidify by standing on a level surface for 5 to 10 minutes at room temperature. Petri dishes may now be used for sampling. If dishes are not to be used the same day as poured, store the covered dishes in an inverted position until you are ready to use them.

> WARNING: Do not allow your fingers to touch the agar medium anytime during preparation or sampling or during disposal afterwards.

3. After the medium has hardened in the dishes, move the dishes to the site where the air will be sampled. At the site, open new paper towels and arrange them on horizontal surfaces where sampling is desired. Preferable sites are outdoors or around a group of people. Lay out one each of the varieties of dishes to be used on the paper towels. Remove covers from dishes. Place the covers, *with tops "up,"* on other newly opened paper towels where they will not be disturbed. Do not invert the covers while dishes are being exposed. (See Figs. 12-2 and 12-3.)

Expose the nutrient surfaces to the air for 15 minutes for adequate collection of bacteria. Replace the dish covers and transfer the covered dishes to appropriate incubators. A minimum of 1 unexposed dish per medium batch should be incubated with the exposed dishes to determine whether there was contamination of the medium during preparation. If contamination is evident, it is not necessary to discard the batch but it should be noted when compiling results.

4. Invert dishes and place in incubator at a temperature of 35°C ± 0.5°C for 24 ± 2 hr. or at 20°C ± 0.5°C for 48 ± 3 hr. If an incubator is not available, the dishes may be placed in a dark space at room temperature (about 20°C) for 48 ± 3 hr.

5. At the end of the incubation period, the total microbial colonies and formations may be counted. (Fig. 12-4 clearly shows how an exposed petri dish looks next to an unexposed dish.) Counting should be done on an approved counting aid, such as the Quebec Colony Counter. If such equipment is not available, counting may be done with one using equivalent magnification and illumination or by using a 1.5 power magnifying glass and counting the colonies against an illuminated black surface. The INTEGRID Quebec Grid Petri dishes are especially helpful here.

The illuminated black surface can be constructed using a sheet of black paper, a supported glass plate and a light source that may be beamed on the black surface but not shining in the eyes of the observer.

6. Report results in counts/ft^2.

Note: Petri dish surface area is approximately $\frac{1}{15}$ ft^2.

7. When counting is completed, plastic petri dishes should be discarded in sealed refuse containers or incinerated. Plastic petri dishes should not be reused; do not attempt to wash and sterilize for later use. Glass petri dishes should have agar removed by scraping the medium into suitable containers and incinerating the agar. Glass dishes should be washed and sterilized for later use. Be especially careful not to touch exposed medium or microorganisms during cleaning or disposal.

When disposal is completed, thoroughly wash hands with soap and water to prevent possible infection.

Note: Some students may wish to proceed with selective sampling and identification of microorganisms. This should be done only under the supervision of your biology teacher.

VI. Records

Keep complete and legible records of (1) date and time of sampling, (2) description of the sampling site, and (3) the number of colonies of microorganisms counted.

VII. References

1. Wells, E. F., Airborne Contagion and Hygiene; Harvard University Press, Cambridge, Mass., 1955.

2. Gregory, P. H., The Microbiology of the Atmosphere; Leonard Hill (Books) Limited, London, Interscience Publishers, Inc., New York, 1961.

3. Standard Methods, Water and Wastewater, American Public Health Association, Inc., New York, 1965.

4. First, M. W., "Controlling Airborne Bacteria—How Well Can It Be Done with Today's Air Sanitation Methods?", Air Engineering, p. 29/33, April, 1960.

5. Standard Methods for the Examination of Dairy Products, American Public Health Association, New York, 1960.

6. Ehlers, V. M., Steel, E. W., Municipal and Rural Sanitation; McGraw-Hill Book Company, New York, 1965.

VIII. Prepared by Eric M. Holt and David J. Romano

APPENDIX

Basic steps in media preparation of dehydrated base (from Standard Methods for the Examination of Dairy Products).

1. Weigh carefully the proper amount of the dehydrated base medium or the correct proportions of the constituent ingredients.

Tryptone glucose yeast agar constituents are as follows:

5.0 grams Peptone-Tryptone

2.5 grams Yeast extract

1.0 grams Glucose (dextrose)

15.0 grams Agar, biological grade

These proportions are correct for each liter of distilled water.

2. Place the desired amount of distilled water in a suitable container (e.g., borosilicate glass or stainless steel).

3. Add the weighed materials to part of the water. Mix. Add the remaining water and mix again.

4. Heat by boiling above an asbestos-centered wire gauze over a free flame or over an electric hotplate, stirring frequently to prevent burning on the bottom of the container. The agar medium should be boiled for 3 minutes. Restore water, if necessary, to compensate for loss by evaporation.

5. Determine pH, either by electrometric or colorimetric methods, and adjust the reaction, if necessary, to 7.0 ± 0.1. Normally this is not necessary with dehydrated base media because they are manufactured so as to give the proper final pH. (For a complete and detailed procedure for pH adjustment, see Standard Methods for Dairy Examination, p. 225–226 or Standard Methods for the Examination of Water and Wastewater.)

6. Distribute media in suitable containers, such as 20×148 mm test tubes, but do not exceed 10–12 ml. per tube. The amount of medium per container should be limited so that at least 2.5 cm. air space is maintained between the container top and medium surface.

7. Sterilize at 121°C (249.8°F) for 15 minutes in an autoclave or in a small pressure cooker set at 15 pounds per square inch pressure for 15 minutes. At the end of the 15 minutes, tubes are ready for storage.

8. To prevent contamination and evaporation of media in tubes during storage, fit tube openings with pliable metal foil, rubber, plastic, parchment or heavy kraft paper. Screw cap containers should be used when available so that contamination and evaporation are substantially reduced. Media should be stored in a dry, relatively cool (preferably refrigerated), dustfree area and should not be exposed to direct sunlight.

9. When media are to be poured from tubes after storage, loosen protective covering and place tubes in boiling water bath to melt agar (10–20 minutes). Allow to cool to 44–46°C (111–113°F); remove protective covering altogether; pass open mouth of tube through open gas flame to insure against contamination, then pour medium into petri dishes as described in procedure previously.

EXPERIMENT NO. 13

Determination of Smoke Shade

I. Object

1. To determine the darkness of smoke being emitted from a stack.
2. To practice the rating of the shade or darkness of smoke according to Ringelmann number.

II. Suitability and Usefulness

1. Suitable for students at junior or senior high school level.
2. Makes the observer more aware of differences in the shade of smoke, thus giving the teacher an opportunity to stress the causes for differences in combustion efficiency.

III. Theory

All combustion processes, involving the burning of materials composed of carbon, hydrogen, and possibly oxygen, will produce only carbon dioxide and water vapor if combustion is complete. Both products are colorless and harmless.

Let us consider the burning of a typical pulverized bituminous coal for steam generation of electric power. Such a fuel might consist of 72% carbon, 5% hydrogen, 1% nitrogen, 9% oxygen, 3% sulfur, and 10% ash. In this instance, we would be creating some gaseous pollution by the production of sulfur dioxide. But if we were able to burn the fuel with 100% efficiency so that our only other products of combustion were carbon dioxide and water vapor, each 100 pounds of the coal would require about 16,000 cubic feet of air supplied at an average temperature of 70°F to provide the necessary oxygen. Under these conditions there should be no visible smoke because all of the carbon would be burned and changed to colorless carbon dioxide gas.

In actual practice it is usually impossible to burn any fuel completely, even when an excess amount of air is supplied. Thus particles of unburned carbon are carried along with the gaseous products and make the gases discharging from the smokestack black or various shades of gray.

The first attempt to gauge the amount of pollution being discharged into the atmosphere was made in 1898 by Maximilian Ringelmann. He devised a series of charts or cards numbered 1 to 5 divided into squares formed by a grid of black lines on a white background. Following introduction into the United States, the number of cards was reduced to four. Width or thickness of lines varies from chart to chart, so that card number 1 represents smoke of very little darkness, equivalent to 20% black while card number 4 represents very dark smoke, equivalent to 80% black. For best results the cards must be held or placed about 50 feet in front of the observer, while he is looking at the smoke coming from the stack. Shade of smoke is compared with the darkness of one of the four cards, and is then graded as Ringelmann No. 1, Ringelmann No. 2, etc.

To overcome the difficulty of placing the Ringelmann chart 50 feet in front of the observer, Power's Microringelmann, a facsimile of the full size Ringelmann, is available. This can be held at arm's length by the observer. Two sets of Ringelmann grids are reproduced on a 3¼" × 5" card. A ½" wide slot is cut between the two sets of grids. The two sides of the Power's Microringelmann are reproduced in Fig. 13-1.

IV. Equipment

1. Supply of Power's Microringelmann, available from Power, 330 West 42nd Street, New York, New York 10036. Cost—35¢ each.

V. Procedure

1. Select a suitable site for observation of the smoke plume being discharged by a factory or power house smoke stack. The observer should be standing not less than 100 feet from the stack and not more than ¼ mile from it. The background immediately beyond the top of the stack should be free of buildings or other dark objects.
2. Hold the lower right hand corner of the Power's Microringelmann between the thumb and index finger, with the reproduced grids toward the observer.
3. Face the stack to be observed, and hold the Power's Microringelmann at arm's length so that you are observing the smoke at the top of the stack through the ½" slot in the card. Be sure the light falling on the card is the same as that falling on the smoke to be observed.

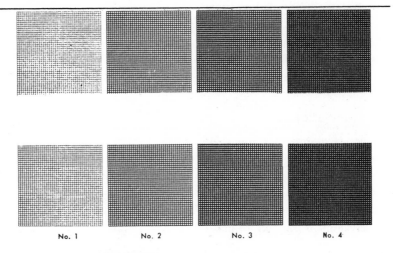

No. 1   No. 2   No. 3   No. 4

Power's MICRORINGELMANN

These grids are a direct facsimile reduction of the standard Ringelmann Chart as issued by the United States Bureau of Mines. Copyright 1954 by McGraw-Hill Publishing Company, Inc. (Publisher of Power) 330 W 42nd St, New York 36, N Y

Price: 35¢ each, discount on quantities

Front side of Power's Ringelmann

Power's **MicroRingelmann** is an accurate photographic reduction of the standard Ringelmann Smoke Chart as published by the United States Bureau of Mines.
For best results, use this card according to the following instructions:

1. Hold chart at arm's length and view smoke through slot provided.
2. Be sure that light shining on chart is the same light that is shining on smoke being examined; for best results, sun should be behind observer.
3. Match smoke as closely as possible with corresponding grid on chart.
4. Enter density of smoke (designated by numbers under each grid) on record sheet; also enter time of each observation.
5. Repeat observations at regular intervals of ¼ or ½ minute.
6. To compute smoke density, use the formula

$$\frac{\text{Equivalent units of No. 1 smoke} \times 0.20}{\text{number of observations}} = \text{percentage smoke density}$$

7. Note and record distance to stack, direction of stack, shape and diameter of stack and speed and direction of wind.

Back side of Power's Ringelmann

Fig. 13-1 — The Power's Microringelmann

4. Move the Power's Microringelmann slowly from side to side until the shade of the smoke matches the shade of one of the pairs of grids.

5. Record the Ringelmann number of the pair of grids which the shade of the smoke matches.

6. Repeat the observations at intervals of ¼ or ½ minute for 15 minutes.

VI. Records and Computations

1. Record the number of observations applicable to each Ringelmann number.

2. Compute the weighted average Ringelmann number of the smoke:

    a. Multiply each Ringelmann number by the number of observations of that Ringelmann number.

    b. Total these products and divide this total by the total number of observations.

    c. The answer may be rounded off to the nearest whole number, or reported to the nearest tenth (one decimal place).

Note: Governmental air pollution control agencies sometimes use a more complicated procedure in determining average degree of smoke shade. But the foregoing computation is adequate for satisfying the objectives of this experiment.

Example:

Ringelmann Number		Number of Observations		Product
1	×	4	=	4
2	×	6	=	12
3	×	10	=	30
4	×	12	=	48
Totals		32		94

Weighted average Ringelmann number = $94/32 = 2.9 = 3$

3. What do you think are the advantages and disadvantages of the Ringelmann chart for determining smoke shade?

VII. References

1. Air Pollution; Barker, Cambi, et al; World Health Organization, 1961.

2. Air Pollution Handbook; Magill, Holden, and Ackley; McGraw-Hill, 1956.

VIII. Prepared by Donald C. Hunter

EXPERIMENT NO. 14

Soiling Properties of the Air— (How Dirty is the Air?)

I. Object

1. To determine whether the atmosphere has sufficient fine particles of solid matter suspended in it to cause soiling of fabrics or other materials through which they pass or with which they might come in contact.

II. Suitability and Usefulness

1. Can be used as a demonstration for younger children and as an experiment by junior and senior high school students.

2. Good as a demonstration project.

3. The experiment demonstrates that the air in which we live and which we breathe is not always as clean as it appears to be.

4. By assigning values to degrees of soiling, the experiment can also be used as a measure of economic loss due to soiling of clothing and other fabrics, and discoloration of buildings and other structures.

5. The experiment may be repeated on successive days to determine whether soiling is worse on some days than on others.

III. Theory

1. Polluted air may contain far greater quantities of suspended solids than clean air. Much of this material is dark in color and can be readily seen when filtered from the air.

2. Light transmittance *or* light reflectance may be used to measure the darkening of a collecting surface due to such fine particles. This experiment is based on light transmittance.

IV. Equipment

1. Small vacuum pump or water aspirator having an air volume capacity of approximately $\frac{3}{4}$ cubic foot per minute.

2. Two pieces of 28-mm outside diameter glass tubing 50 to 75-mm long, with 1.2-mm wall thickness.*

3. Window screen—disc cut 28-mm in diameter.

4. Two rubber stoppers to fit glass tubing. Each stopper to have an 8-mm hole in center.

5. Two 75-mm pieces of 8-mm outside diameter glass tubing.*

6. Whatman #41 filter paper—28 mm diameter discs.

7. Rubber band, 1-inch wide, to fit snugly around 28-mm tubing, or 1-inch wide masking tape.

8. Burette stand with a 3-finger clamp.

9. Plastic (Tygon or Nalgon) or rubber tubing to connect filter to vacuum pump and to act as a probe to collect outdoor air.

10. Flowmeter (rotameter) of appropriate range, or a wet or dry gas meter if available. A critical orifice of proper size may be used to control air flow at the maximum rate desired.

11. Glass bottle (1-gal capacity) fitted with 2-hole rubber stopper containing one long and one short piece of 8-mm glass tubing. The bottle should be nested in a corrugated board box for safety.

12. Small metal or plastic funnel.

V. Procedure-Assembly of apparatus (see Fig. 14-1)

1. Set the screen on top of one piece of 28-mm tubing (now called cylinder #1).

2. Place a filter paper disc on the screen.

3. Place the other piece of 28-mm tubing (cylinder #2) on top of the filter paper, press the two cylinders together, and make an air-tight seal with the rubber band or with masking tape.

4. Insert a small glass tube in a hole through each rubber stopper. Place one stopper in the lower end of cylinder #1 and the other stopper in the upper end of cylinder #2. Mount the assembly in the burette stand with cylinder #2 in the upper position.

5. Using plastic or rubber tubing, connect cylinder #1 to the lower tap on the rotameter or to the

*Be sure glass tubing is cut square and the ends fire polished to avoid cut fingers.

inlet of other type of flow measuring device. Connect the outlet of the rotameter or other flowmeter to the inlet side (long glass tube) of the 1-gallon bottle. (This bottle evens out any fluctuations due to the vacuum pump. It is called a surge or buffer bottle.)

6. Similarly connect the outlet tube from the surge bottle to the inlet tap of the vacuum pump or other source of vacuum.

7. Connect a long piece of plastic or rubber tubing to the inlet end of cylinder #2, and pass the other end through a window. The stem of the funnel should be inserted in the tubing hanging outside. The funnel should hang upside down to prevent rain from entering the tubing.

VI. Procedure—operation

1. Start the vacuum pump and record the time. Measure and record the rate of air flow.

2. Allow air to pass through the filter for two hours or as long as required to darken the filter paper noticeably.

3. Measure and record the rate of air flow. Stop the vacuum pump and record the time.

4. Dismantle and observe the soiling of the filter paper.

5. If a photometer to measure transmittance of light through the soiled filter paper is available, a quantitative evaluation of the amount of soiling can be made. (Physics students may be interested in investigating and building a simple means of measuring light transmittance through the tape.)

VII. Quantitative Evaluation

Theory—The amount of discoloration on the filter paper is approximately proportional to the quantity of solid particles suspended in the air. This makes it possible to relate the decrease in light transmittance through the paper to the amount of dirt particles collected on it. The light transmittance of the paper can be measured with a photometer before and after filtering the air by placing the clean filter disc and, later, the exposed filter disc against the photometer window and noting the intensity of light transmitted in each test.

From these measurements the optical density of the soiled filter paper can be computed in COH's. The COH is an abbreviation for Coefficient of Haze, and one COH unit represents an optical density of 0.01. The optical density of the

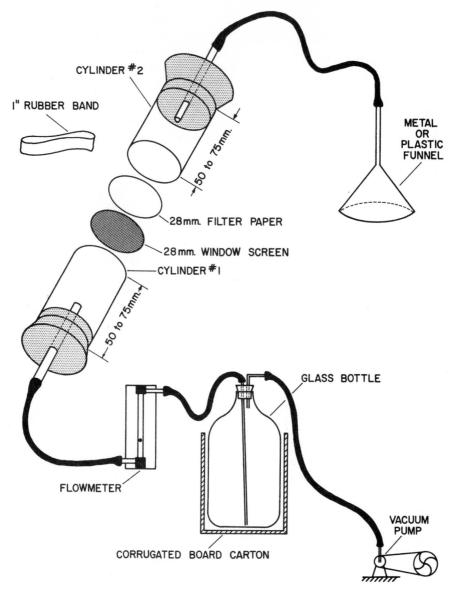

Fig. 14-1. Assembly For Sampling Air For Soiling Properties

deposit or soiling is the logarithm to the base 10 of the ratio of the intensity of light transmitted through the clean filter paper to the intensity of the light transmitted through the soiled filter paper. In terms of percentage, it can also be the ratio of percent transmittance through the clean paper (considered as 100%) to the percent transmittance through the soiled paper. Therefore,

$$\frac{I_o}{I_t} = \log_{10} \frac{100\%}{\%T}$$

where,

I_0 = average light intensity transmitted through clean filter paper,

I_t = light intensity transmitted through the soiled paper, and

$\%T$ = percent light transmitted through the soiled paper when the light transmittance through clean paper is considered as 100%.

Since $\log_{10}$ of 100 = 2.0, we have

$$O.D. = 2.0 - \log \%T$$

By definition, one COH unit equals an optical density of 0.01. Thus, the number of COH's represented by the actual O.D. found equals O.D./0.01 = 100 × (2.0 − log %T).

COH unit measurements are usually expressed as COH's per 1,000 linear feet of air passed through the filter paper. The concept of linear flow, upon which the expression COH's per 1,000 feet is based, considers that through each point on the surface of the filter a long stream of air passes leaving its load of dirt particles deposited. One might think of the sample as a long column of air the same diameter as the diameter of the exposed filter paper and with a volume equal to the measured volume of the air sample.

Computations

1. Volume of air = $R_2 − R_1$ (for dry or wet gas meter),

R_2 = final reading in cubic feet

R_1 = original reading in cubic feet

or, volume of air = $\dfrac{t(F_1 + F_2)}{2}$ (for rotameter or critical orifice).

F_1 = initial flow rate in cubic feet per minute

F_2 = final flow rate in cubic feet per minute

t = sampling time in minutes

Corrections for Temperature and Pressure (if desired)

The value $R_2 − R_1$ for the gas meter should be corrected for temperature and pressure according to the Charles' and Boyle's Laws.

Each F value for the rotameter or orifice should first be corrected to what it would be at the standard temperature and pressure at which the measuring device was calibrated:

$$F_s = F\sqrt{\frac{T_s}{T} \cdot \frac{P}{P_s}}$$

2. Area $= \dfrac{\pi d^2}{4}$, where d is the inside diameter of the cylinder in feet.

$$\text{ft.} = \text{mm.} \times \frac{\text{cm.}}{\text{mm.}} \times \frac{\text{in.}}{\text{cm.}} \times \frac{\text{ft.}}{\text{in.}}$$

3. Linear feet of air $= \dfrac{\text{Volume}}{\text{Area}} = L$

4. COH's per 1000 feet $= \dfrac{(2.0 − \log \%T) \times 100}{L/1000}$

$$= \frac{(2.0 − \log \%T) \times 100 \times 1000}{L}$$

$$= \frac{(2.0 − \log \%T) \times 10^5}{L}$$

VIII. References

1. "Experiments for the Science Classroom," Taylor, Miller, and Lyon; State of California, Department of Health.

2. Theory of the Flowrator; Fischer and Porter Company, Hatboro, Pennsylvania.

IX. Prepared by Donald C. Hunter

EXPERIMENT NO. 15

Collection of Wind-Blown Particles

I. Object

1. To determine a measure of the number of larger particles in the air which are carried on the wind.

2. To examine and practice another method of collecting solid particles.

II. Suitability and Usefulness

1. Easy for a junior high school experiment.

2. Demonstrates to students the size range of particles which may be wind-blown.

3. Teaches measurements by visual comparison with standard photographs.

III. Theory

Wind-blown particles, which can be readily seen with the naked eye after collection, range in size from approximately 20 to 100 microns. (Students

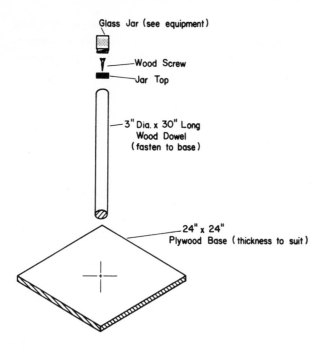

Fig. 15-1. Assembly For Collecting Wind-Blown Particles

should look up and memorize the definition of a micron.) Since the movement of wind-blown particles is more horizontal than vertical, a good collecting surface is a vertical plane. Sticky paper, to which the particles will adhere, provides such a surface.

By wrapping the vertical plane of sticky paper around a small glass jar, it is possible to note from which direction more or less of the particles were blown.

IV. Equipment

1. Fassons Pli-A-Print R-135 adhesive paper, with removable protective release liner M78. (Obtainable from Fasson Products Division of Avery Paper Co., 250 Chester Street, Painesville, Ohio. The adhesive is an acrylic latex. Sheets are $25\frac{1}{2}'' \times 20''$, can be cut to $2'' \times 10''$ for use.)

2. Glass jar, approximately $2\frac{3}{4}$ inches diameter $\times$ $3\frac{1}{4}$ inches high, with metal or plastic screw-on lid. (Specifications are: #4378-30 bottle, solid, storage, extra-wide mouth, threaded neck, flint glass, short form; can be obtained from local laboratory supplier.)

3. Stand to hold jar in up-side-down position, while screwed into an extra lid. An extra lid can be tacked to the stand in an up-side-down position so that the jar can be screwed into it.

Fig. 15-2. Photographic Standard (reproduction)

This might be constructed in the school shop from the accompanying sketch (see Fig. 15-1).

4. Spray can of clear lacquer. (Jap-A-Lac 4010 clear acrylic, or equivalent; any local supplier.)

5. Photographic standard for particles per square inch (Fig. 15-2), obtainable from Technical Associates For Industry, Inc., P. O. Box 116, Park Ridge, New Jersey 07656.

V. Procedure

Set up the stand, for holding the glass jar, on a flat and safe area of your school roof. You should keep as far away from obstructions as possible so that the wind will have a clear sweep from all directions.

Fasten one end of the 2″ × 10″ strip of sticky paper to the jar with a small piece of scotch tape. Wrap the paper around the jar. Remove the release liner to expose the sticky surface. With the release liner removed, the overlapped ends of the paper will stick together so that the paper stays in position on the jar.

Place the jar in the holder and mark the paper to indicate the side or position facing North. Leave the jar exposed for seven days. Then spray the paper with a clear lacquer to fix the particles collected and to avoid having additional particles adhere to the paper.

Take the exposed sample to the laboratory and divide the sample into eight equal parts representing the eight principal points of the compass. Mark the proper compass point on each part of the sample. Then compare each part with the accompanying standard photographs. Estimate the number of particles collected per square inch from each direction.

VI. References

1. Interstate Air Pollution Effects Surveillance Network, Field Investigations Section, Abatement Branch, Division of Air Pollution, Robert A. Taft Sanitary Engineering Center, Cincinnati, Ohio 45226.

2. Selection of Adhesive-Coated Materials for Particulate Sampling, by Pritchard, Schumann, and Gruber; J. of Air Pollution Control Association, May 1967.

3. The use of Sticky Paper in an Air Pollution Monitoring Program; Gruber and Jutze; J. of Air Pollution Control Association, August 1957.

VII. Prepared by Donald C. Hunter.

Note: The reproduction of the standard particles per square inch in Fig. 15-2 is not a true reproduction of the photographic standards, and should not be used for measuring or estimating the number of particles collected per square inch of sticky paper.

EXPERIMENT NO. 16

Determination of Dustfall or Settleable Particulates

I. Object

1. To determine the weight of solid particles settling from the air onto a particular area of the ground or other surface during a given period of time.

II. Suitability and Usefulness

1. Can be used as an experiment at the junior and senior high school levels. (In some instances, the teacher may find a less precise determination suitable for younger children. This can be accomplished by modifying and simplifying the procedure.)

2. Good as a demonstration project.

3. The experiment demonstrates that the force of gravity acts on small particles as well as larger objects.

4. By considering possible sources, the experiment should indicate to students that particles are carried horizontally by air movement while falling vertically by gravity.

5. To those students living relatively near sources of solid particles, such as dusts and smoke, the experiment should help explain some of the deposits they find on porches and cars.

III. Theory

Dusts and other solid particles present in the ocean of air in which we live have many sources. Some are of natural origin. These may be fine particles of dry soil or grains of pollen which are picked up by the wind. Others originate from man's activity. Construction and demolition activities and combustion and industrial processes are examples. Such sources may be large or small—a large power plant or a home heating plant, a large dump or backyard burning of refuse. Many small sources can be the equivalent of a large source.

These airborne solid particles are of many sizes and shapes. Those small enough to defy the pull of gravity remain suspended in the atmosphere. But the larger ones settle to the first surface that will hold them. This experiment deals only with the larger particles.

IV. Equipment

1. A glass jar with screw lid. Jar should have a capacity of about one gallon. A pickle jar having a mouth diameter of about 4 inches is satisfactory. A more exacting specification would be Brockway jar #1875, which can be purchased from jobbers.
2. A stand with brackets to hold the jar firmly in an upright position. To help avoid collection of bird droppings, a wire ring 15 inches in diameter may be supported about 6 inches above the jar.
3. Screen, 20-mesh, 5-inch diameter.
4. Glass funnel, 6-inch diameter.
5. Glass beakers, assorted sizes.
6. Graduated cylinders, assorted sizes.
7. Pipettes, assorted sizes.
8. Steam bath or hot plate.
9. Oven with temperature control, for use in the 100°C range.
10. Desiccator.
11. Analytical balance, 200-gram capacity, precision ±0.05 mg.
12. Glass stirring rods.
13. Policemen, rubber or polyethylene.

V. Reagents

1. Zephiran chloride, 1:1000 aqueous solution, to retard growth of algae in any rain water collecting in the jar.
2. Sodium lauryl sulfate, U.S.P., for use as a wetting agent to help remove all solid matter from the collection jar.

    a. 1% stock solution. Dissolve 1 gram of sodium lauryl sulfate in distilled water and dilute to 100 ml with distilled water. Allow foaming to subside before diluting to final volume.

    b. 0.025% working solution. Dilute 25 ml of stock solution to 1 liter with distilled water.

VI. Procedure

1. Preparation of jar

    a. Wash jar, rinse with distilled water, and drain dry.

    b. Add 5 ml of the zephiran chloride 1:1000 aqueous solution to the jar. This retards growth of algae.

    c. Place lid on jar and screw it on sufficiently tight to prevent leakage.

2. Sampling procedure

    a. At the beginning of the sampling period, transport the prepared jar to the sampling site and set it top up, in the holding bracket on the sampling stand. The sampling site should preferably be on a flat portion of the school roof which is safely accessible, and should be well away from any superstructures which would create eddy currents to prevent natural settling. Remove and save the lid. Record the date sampling starts.

    b. Expose the jar for the standard sampling period of 30 days. For convenience, a tolerance of ±4 days is considered satisfactory for a valid sample. In other words, the open jar may be exposed for a time period of 26 to 34 days. If a series of samples is to be taken, it is helpful to have sampling periods conform to calendar months.

    c. At the end of the sampling period, replace the lid and take the exposed jar to the laboratory. If desired, set out a new jar at the same time.

    d. Record the date on which sampling ends.

3. Analytical procedure for determination of total settleable solid particles

    a. Remove any extraneous matter, such as leaves, twigs, or paper, which cannot be considered settleable particles. Do this by transferring all of the sample through the 20-mesh screen into a beaker. A funnel may be used to hold the screen. Use measured amounts of hot distilled water as necessary to transfer the sample and to rinse the extraneous material on the screen.

b. Discard the larger pieces.

c. Scrub the inside surface of the jar with a policeman and wash it down with measured amounts of hot distilled water. Pour the washings through the screen into the beaker. Any tar-like substances adhering to the inner surface of the jar or to the screen should be removed by using a measured amount of the 0.025% sodium lauryl sulfate solution (up to 20 ml) to help loosen it.

d. Discard the residue on the screen.

e. In a beaker of suitable size, prepare a reagent blank containing the same amounts of algaecide, distilled water, and sodium lauryl sulfate solution as were used for preparing and transferring the sample being analyzed.

f. Place the beakers (containing sample and blank) on the steam bath or hot plate and evaporate to a small volume of liquid.

Caution: If a hot plate is used, do not allow the sample to boil. Do not allow the sample to evaporate to dryness.

g. Transfer the residual liquid and solids of the sample and of the blank to individual 50-ml beakers which have been heated in the oven at 103° to 105°C for two hours, cooled in a desiccator, and weighed preferably to the nearest 0.1 mg.

Use a policeman and measured amounts of hot distilled water to wash the entire residue from each beaker into individual 50-ml beakers. Up to 20 ml of 0.025% sodium lauryl sulfate solution per beaker may be used, if necessary, to facilitate the transfer. Several washings may be necessary.

Note: Following this transfer, the sample and the blank shall *each* contain the same amounts of distilled water and sodium lauryl sulfate solution.

h. Place the 50-ml beakers with residues and washings on a steam bath or in the oven at 103° to 105°C and evaporate all visible water. Then dry the beakers with residues in an oven at 103° to 105°C for 2 hours.

i. Cool the dried beakers with residues to room temperature in a desiccator and weigh each to the nearest 0.1 mg. Subtract the tare weight of each beaker from its gross weight to obtain net weight of residue in each beaker.

j. Subtract the net weight of residue in the blank beaker from that in the sample beaker. This is the weight of total settleable particles collected in the sample.

VII. Computations

1. Sampling period. From the dates recorded, determine the number of days during which the sample was being collected.

2. Calculate the area of exposure in square centimeters from the inside diameter of the jar mouth, measured to the nearest millimeter.

$$A = \frac{\pi d^2}{4} = .785d^2 = \pi r^2.$$
$$1 \text{ mm.} = 0.1 \text{cm.}$$

3. Compute and report the total settleable particulates collected in 30 days to the nearest 0.01 mg./cm.^{2} This is expressed as mg./cm.^{2}/30 days.

Note: If the sampling period was other than 30 days it will be necessary to compute the final result on the basis of a 30-day sampling period. Do this as follows:

$$\frac{\text{mg.}}{\text{cm.}^2} \times \frac{30}{\text{actual days}}$$

Note: The student may be able to visualize better the total weight of particles settling to the ground by thinking in terms of pounds falling on a ground area of one acre (a square roughly 200 feet on each side). The conversion would be as follows:

$$\frac{\text{mg.}}{\text{cm.}^2} \times \frac{\text{lbs.}}{\text{mg.}} \times \frac{\text{m.}^2}{\text{acre}} \times \frac{\text{cm.}^2}{\text{m.}^2} = \frac{\text{lbs.}}{\text{acre}}$$

4. The results may be compared with your local or state ambient air quality standards. The teacher may wish to have a multiple type of experiment conducted to determine reproducibility.

VIII. References

1. "Method for Examination of Settleable Solids in Air"; New York State Department of Health, Division of Laboratories and Research.

2. Air Pollution Handbook; Magill, Holden, and Ackley; McGraw-Hill; 1956.

3. Air Pollution; Barker, Cambi, Catcott, et. al.; World Health Organization; 1961.

4. Air Pollution, Arthur C. Stern, 2nd edition, Academic Press, 1968.

IX. Prepared by Donald C. Hunter

EXPERIMENT NO. 17

Aerosol Filtration

I. Object

1. To demonstrate the filtration efficiency of various filtering media.

II. Suitability and Usefulness

1. Illustrate a technique used in air sampling and stack gas cleaning.

2. Students can be made aware that air and gas filtration is not a simple sieving action.

III. Theory and Background

The filtration of aerosol particles by means of fibrous and other porous materials depends, at least initially, on mechanisms other than mechanically separating the particles on matrices whose dimensions are smaller than the diameter of the particles (sieving). These mechanisms include particle inertia, interception, Brownian diffusion, gravity and electrostatic forces.

Inertia produces deposition (impaction) of aerosol particles on obstacles in their path since, as the airstream expands and moves around the obstacle, the particle, because of its inertia, tends to continue in a straight line and impact upon the obstacle. (In many filters the obstacle, such as fibers, are separated from each other by dimensions many times their diameters, even though the filter looks dense to the naked eye. The aerosol particles, in turn, may be very much smaller in diameter than the diameters of the fiber. In effect, the aerosol particle is, most of the time, very far away, in terms of its size, from a fiber.) The inertial effect increases with increasing particle diameter, with increasing velocity through the filter and with decreasing obstacle (fiber) diameter.

The interception effect is related to the inertial one and differs only in that it is related directly to the particle diameter. A particle which would pass an obstacle if it were very small may be intercepted by the edge of the obstacle if its diameter were larger.

Brownian diffusion (the motion due to bombardment of the aerosol particles by air molecules) is an important collection mechanism for very fine particles. This random motion brings particles close enough to contact obstacles even though their inertia is so low they would tend to flow around the obstacle. The diffusion effect increases with decreasing particle diameter, with decreasing velocity through the filter and with decreasing obstacle diameter.

Gravity is an important effect in aerosol filtration only when the particle's mass is sufficient to cause motion toward an obstacle such that a particle will contact the surface of the obstacle even though its inertia would tend to cause it to flow around the obstacle. The gravity effect is important only for comparatively large diameter particles.

Electrostatic forces can be quite important in aerosol filtration for small diameter particles freshly generated in such a way as to create significant surface charges on the particles, e.g., smoke particles. In addition, for some filters surface charges generated on the obstacle surfaces also aid collection, although such surface charges are usually short-lived. There are several electrostatic forces which can operate during aerosol filtration, the most important of which, for uncharged filters, are aerosol image forces and the space charge effect. The former is due to disruption of the electrical field surrounding the particles because of the presence of the obstacles. The latter is due to mutual repulsion of like-charged aerosol particles. Electrostatic effects increase with increasing particle charge, with decreasing particle diameter and with decreasing velocity through the filter. (The effect of obstacle diameter is too complex for discussion here.)

For very small aerosol particles, such as freshly generated tobacco smoke (0.5 micron in diameter, or smaller) the overall effect of velocity is such that filtration efficiency increases as the velocity through the filter decreases (diffusion and electrostatic effects predominate). This is true for comparatively loosely packed filters such as laboratory filter paper or cotton cloth. For filters which are essentially sieves, such as membrane filters of small pore size, the effect of filtering velocity should be negligible.

IV. Equipment

1. Aerosol Field Monitors with Millipore filters, catalog No. MAWP 037 AO, Filter type AA,

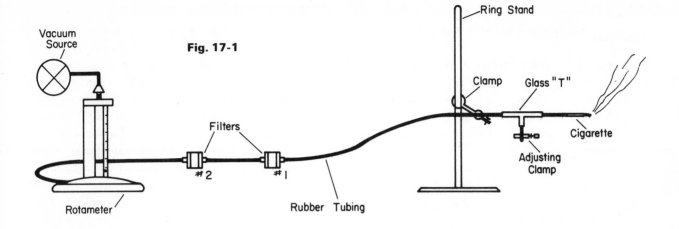

Fig. 17-1

Labels in figure: Vacuum Source, Ring Stand, Clamp, Glass "T", Cigarette, Adjusting Clamp, Filters, #2, #1, Rotameter, Rubber Tubing

white, plain, $30 per carton of 50—purchase from Millipore Corporation, Bedford, Massachusetts, 01730.

2. Aerosol field monitors, plastic holder only, catalog No. MOOO 37 AO, Aerosol monitor cases, $8 per carton of 50—purchase from Millipore Corporation.

3. Replacements: Millipore filters catalog No. MFAAWP 37, filter type AA, white, plain, $18.50 per package of 100—purchase from Millipore Corporation.

4. Replacements: Millipore filter support pads, catalog No. AP 100 3700, $3 per package of 100—purchase from Millipore Corporation.

5. Analytical balance capable of weighing to 0.0001 gram.

6. A flowmeter with range of 0–5 liters of air per minute, such as Dual-Scale Flowmeter, catalog No. 8202, $11.50—purchase from Gelman Instrument Company, P.O. Box 1448, Ann Arbor, Michigan, 48106; or Flowmeter Model Series 520, Ordering No. 23, $8—purchase from F. W. Dwyer Manufacturing Co., P.O. Box 373, Michigan City, Indiana, 46360.

7. A source of vacuum which can be regulated, such as a laboratory vacuum line or an aspirator fixture connected to a laboratory faucet.

8. Glass tee.

9. ¼ inch or ³⁄₁₆ inch inside diameter rubber tubing about 3 feet long.

10. Screw clamp for adjusting air flow through tubing.

11. Ringstand and clamp.

12. Filter media of various kinds such as Whatman #41 laboratory filter papers, cotton cloth,

nylon cloth, and absorbant cotton batting, cut to shape so as to fit in a Millipore field monitor (37 mm. diameter).

13. Unfiltered cigarettes.

V. Procedure

1. Disassemble 2 Millipore field monitors and carefully weigh each membrane filter to "4 decimal places" (for example, 0.0546 gram). Reassemble field monitors (taping sections together may be necessary). Use forceps to hold filter.

2. Connect apparatus (Fig. 17-1) in the following order (preferably inside of a laboratory hood):

   a. In one end of 2 inch length of tubing insert cigarette, attach other end of tubing to glass tee.

   b. To second branch of glass tee attach 2 inch length of tubing and attach screw clamp.

   c. Connect inlet of one field monitor (test filter) to the third branch of glass tee with rubber tubing (6 inches of tubing should suffice).

   d. Connect inlet of second (or "back-up") field monitor to the outlet of the first field monitor with 2 or 3 inches of rubber tubing.

   e. Connect the outlet of the back-up field monitor to the inlet (lower connection) of the flowmeter.

   f. Connect the outlet of flowmeter to the vacuum source.

3. Ignite the tobacco (screw clamp should be open to permit air to bypass the cigarette).

4. Establish and maintain an air flow reading on the flowmeter of about 3.0 liters per minute and quickly adjust screw clamp to increase air flow through the cigarette to a slow, steady burning

rate. Operate for 10 minutes or until air flow cannot be maintained at original setting. Use a stopwatch.

5. Carefully remove Millipore filters and weigh again, handling filter with forceps.

6. Determine the weight of smoke collected on each filter, the total flow of air in liters, and the face velocity across the filter (air flow divided by filtering area).

7. Assuming that the second filter collects all that escapes the first filter, calculate an efficiency for the test filter. (Since both filters are essentially sieves of low pore size (0.8 microns), efficiency of the first filter should be close to 100%.)

8. Repeat the above procedure using 2 or 3 different fibrous filter media (filter paper, cloth, cotton fiber, etc.) as the first filter and a Millipore filter as the second filter. Determine the filter efficiency by comparing the weight of smoke collected on the first filter with the sum of the smoke weights found on both the test filter and the backup Millipore filter. Calculate the smoke concentration upstream and immediately downstream of the test filter. Express in milligrams per cubic meter of air.

9. Repeat the series of tests using flow rates of 1.6 and 0.6 lpm. Plot filter efficiency for each filter media vs. air velocity across the filter face.

10. From the shape of the efficiency-velocity curve draw conclusions as to the main filtering mechanisms for each filter.

VI. Prepared by Dr. A. D. Brandt

EXPERIMENT NO. 18

Orsat Analysis of a Gas Sample

I. Object

1. To understand the basic operations and concepts of the Orsat apparatus in establishing the concentrations of three gases in a typical gas mixture.

II. Suitability and Usefulness

1. Excellent as a laboratory experiment, demonstration, or project in a chemistry or physics course.

2. The sample used in the analysis can vary to include a wide variety of process emissions and ambient air conditions.

3. Provides a practical demonstration of gas absorption by a suitable liquid.

4. Demonstrates usefulness of a head of liquid in moving fluids in a closed system.

III. Theory

Gas analysis provides the subject matter for a myriad of articles, brochures, and textbooks. Gases are produced by a wide variety of commercial, industrial, and biological combustion processes. Some of these gases are air contaminants. Such gases may be emitted from steam generating boilers, incinerators, automobiles, anaerobic digestion of organic wastes, and furnace boilers.

There are various and sundry gas analysis apparatus available to the scientist and engineer to measure the percentages of specific gases available in a composite sample. The different apparatus are usually designed or modified to measure a specific gas or gases and the analyst must research the literature to determine which apparatus will be most economically and practically feasible to his specific analysis problem.

The Orsat type volumetric gas analyzer can be used to determine the partial gas composition of the atmosphere, of an automobile exhaust, or of the effluent from an ordinary oil furnace, depending upon the preparation of the appropriate reactant solutions and specific modifications by the analyst. Most frequently, the Orsat apparatus is used to measure combustion efficiency by determining the percent carbon dioxide, oxygen, and carbon monoxide present in a gas mixture. The remainder, usually considered to be nitrogen, is obtained by difference.

The speed and efficiency with which an Orsat analysis can be run depends on the apparatus set up, the leveling bottle positions, the optimum absorption time and the numbered passes needed for complete absorption. These factors can best be learned through a thorough understanding of the operational procedure and sufficient analytic experience.

There are two types of errors involved in any experimentation. The first type is called experimental errors and they are due to conditions inherent in the operational procedure and instrumentation. The second type of error is called personal error and involves mistakes and carelessness on the part of the analyst. Examples of the first type include temperature variations, use of solutions whose reactive capacity is not 100 percent, and errors due to barometric changes. Examples of the second include carelessness in sampling, leakage due to unclean or excessively greased stopcocks, and failure to adjust the leveling bottle before readings are taken. Students should practice good analytical techniques to avoid as much as possible those errors which may lead to misleading results.

IV. Equipment

1. Orsat Analyzer (see sketch, Fig. 18-1).

V. Reagents (Procedures of Mixing are in Table 1)

1. Potassium Hydroxide Solution—for pipette No. 1.
2. Alkaline Pyrogallate Solution—for pipette No. 2.
3. Acid Cuprous Chloride Solution—for pipette No. 3.

VI. Procedure

Assemble the Orsat analyzer with the prepared reagents in the pipettes as illustrated in Fig. 18-1.
1. With the stopcocks of the manifold turned so that the sampled gas does not enter the pipettes, take a 100 ml sample from the atmosphere by opening the stopcock to the atmosphere and lowering the leveling bottle. Flush the sample back to the atmosphere. Repeat this process three times and return the sample of gas to the 100 ml mark and close stopcock.
2. Test for a leak in the system by raising the leveling bottle to the highest possible level and hold-

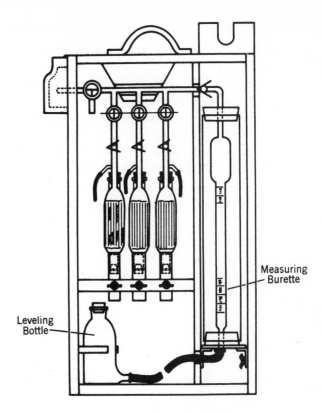

Fig. 18-1. Orsat Gas Analyzer

Measuring Burette

Leveling Bottle

ing for five minutes. After allowing to stand, the reading should not differ by more than 0.2 ml. Repeat this testing procedure by holding the leveling bottle at the lowest possible level.
3. Open the stopcock of the KOH pipette. (It is usually found best to raise the leveling bottle slightly before connecting the bottle to the KOH pipette. This slight over-pressure prevents any rise of KOH into the manifold.)
4. Pass the gas into the KOH pipette by raising the liquid in the burette to the lower part of the capillary inlet. Return the gas to the burette by lowering the leveling bottle until the KOH level rises to the mark on the pipette stem. (Caution: Decrease the rate of lowering the leveling bottle as the KOH level approaches the capillary portion of the pipette.) Repeat this passage and return of gas to and from the KOH pipette three more times. Read the volume of the gas in the burette after the fourth pass. Continue with the same procedure, reading the volume after each pass until two successive readings are the same, indicating complete removal of carbon dioxide. Record the volume of the residual gas. *Close the stopcock of the KOH pipette.*

5. Record the percent of CO_2 in the gas sample. (This is determined by subtracting the final reading of step 4 from 100.)

6. Repeat step 4 for O_2 and CO using the alkaline pyrogallate solution and the acid cuprous chloride solution, respectively. Read the percentage of O_2 and CO found.

7. Determine the amount of assumed N_2 in the atmospheric sample. This percentage is found by adding the individual percentages of CO_2, O_2, and CO found and then subtracting the total from 100.

8. Discharge residual gas.

9. Repeat steps 1–9 using a sample from the exhaust of an automobile or from the effluent of an oil furnace. A sampling hole in the school furnace pipe may be used.

VII. References

1. Jacobs, M. B. "The Chemical Analysis of Air Pollutants," Interscience Publishers, Inc., New York, 1960, pp. 343–350.

2. Mullen, P. W. "Modern Gas Analysis," Interscience Publishers, Inc., New York, 1955, pp. 102–118.

3. Sawyer, C. N. "Chemistry for Sanitary Engineers" McGraw-Hill Book Company, Inc., New York, 1960, pp. 343–347.

VIII. Prepared by Daniel M. Barolo

TABLE 1—PROCEDURES FOR MIXING SOLUTIONS*

Reagent I—Potassium Hydroxide Solution for Absorbing CO_2.

Dissolve 500 g of commercial KOH in one liter of H_2O. The mixing container must be able to withstand the heat of solution; therefore, do not use ordinary glass bottles or heat the solution while mixing. Allow to cool and store in a rubber stopped bottle. One ml absorbs 40 ml of CO_2.

Reagent II—Alkaline Pyrogallate Solution for Absorbing O_2.

Weigh 25 g of pyrogallic acid and put it in a reagent bottle. Dissolve 500 g of KOH in one liter of H_2O as in reagent I. Pour 500 ml of the KOH solution into the reagent bottle and mix. Do not attempt to store the mixture but rather store the separate solutions in rubber stoppered bottles until the time of the experiment. One ml will absorb 2 ml of O_2.

Reagent III—Acid Cuprous Chloride for Absorbing CO

Measure 180 g of cuprous chloride and mix with 1 liter of concentrated HCl. Keep solution from contact with air. Insert clean copper metal wires or strips into the stock solution to maintain the copper solution in the cuprous state. These strips should extend throughout the solution and should be a yellowish-green color. One ml will absorb 1 ml of CO.

*From Reference No. 1.

EXPERIMENT NO. 19

Determination of Sulfation Properties of the Air by the Lead Peroxide Candle —Gravimetric Method

I. Object

1. To determine a measure of the amount of sulfur dioxide present in the air resulting from the sulfation of lead peroxide.

2. To demonstrate to the student by color change that a chemical reaction has taken place merely by exposure of lead peroxide.

II. Suitability and Usefulness

1. Can be used as a demonstration project by junior high school science students.

2. Can be used by chemistry students as a qualitative analysis by identification of barium sulfate precipitate.

3. Can be used by chemistry students as a quantitative analysis to determine the weight of sulfate ion produced per square centimeter of exposed lead peroxide surface during the exposure period.

4. The total experiment is composed of several parts in preparation and determination. It can thus be spread over laboratory periods. Break points or pauses are noted.

III. Theory

Sulfur dioxide in sufficient concentration in the atmosphere is a hazard to human health and an economic loss with respect to many kinds of vegetation and building materials. It is one of the most widespread of gaseous air contaminants. It is produced during the combustion of most fuels and in the processing of sulfur-bearing materials.

One inexpensive means of determining a rough measure of the amount of sulfur dioxide present is to take advantage of its reaction with lead peroxide at a uniform and convenient rate to form lead sulfate, which can then be reacted with barium chloride to form an insoluble barium sulfate precipitate capable of being measured easily by weighing.

$$SO_2 + PbO_2 = PbSO_4$$
$$PbSO_4 + BaCl_2 = PbCl_2 + BaSO_4$$

The lead peroxide candle, as it is called, is exposed for approximately 30 days and is thus a good sampling companion for the jar collecting settleable particulates (Experiment No 16). The "candle" is actually a glass tube or test tube wrapped with 4"-wide surgical gauze. The outside surface of the gauze is coated with a paste containing lead peroxide. The candle is exposed to the air and protected from rain and snow in a small louvered shelter. Sulfur dioxide, and possibly sulfuric acid mist, in a rectangular section of air of infinite length passing through the shelter for 30 days, according to wind directions comes in contact with the lead peroxide. The first chemical reaction written above takes place with respect to sulfur dioxide.

The result in milligrams of SO_4 ion per square centimeter of reacting surface per 30 days is known as the rate of sulfation.

IV. Equipment

1. Pyrex tube, 32 millimeters outside diameter $\times$ 5½ inches long, with fire-polished ends. Or, a test tube of similar size.

2. Gauze bandage, sterile, 4 inches nominal width $\times$ 16¼ inches long.

3. Glass olive jar, 16-oz, and appurtenances (see Fig. 19-1).

4. Shelter, louvered, aluminum on a suitable pipe stand. Can be purchased from sources such as Research Appliance Co., Route 8 and Craighead Road, Allison Park, Pennsylvania 15101. Or, it can be fabricated in the school shop from aluminum pie tins about 7 inches diameter according to Fig. 19-2.

5. Hot plate.

6. Steam bath.

7. Oven equipped with temperature control.

8. Desiccator.

9. Source of vacuum for filtering.

10. Filtering apparatus, such as suction flask with adapter to hold a Gooch crucible.

11. Gooch crucible, 40-ml. capacity.

12. Glass funnel, 5-inch diameter.

13. Beakers, assorted sizes.

14. Graduated cylinders, assorted sizes.

15. Pipettes, graduated, assorted sizes.

16. Ring-Stand with extension clamp.

17. Watch glasses, 5 to 6-inch diameter.

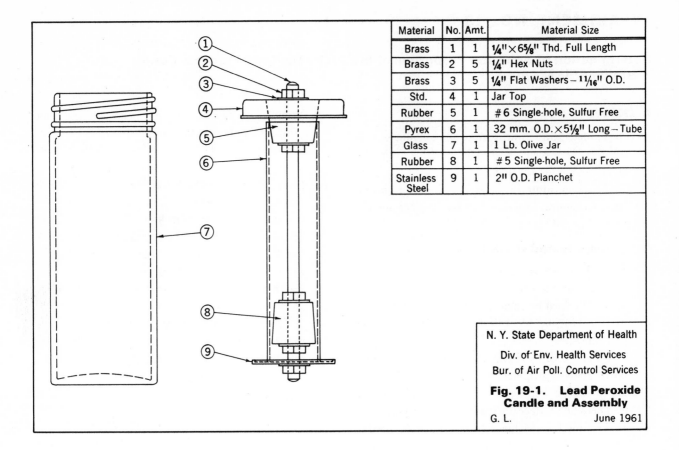

Material	No.	Amt.	Material Size
Brass	1	1	$\frac{1}{4}$" × $6\frac{5}{8}$" Thd. Full Length
Brass	2	5	$\frac{1}{4}$" Hex Nuts
Brass	3	5	$\frac{1}{4}$" Flat Washers — $\frac{11}{16}$" O.D.
Std.	4	1	Jar Top
Rubber	5	1	#6 Single-hole, Sulfur Free
Pyrex	6	1	32 mm. O.D. × $5\frac{1}{2}$" Long — Tube
Glass	7	1	1 Lb. Olive Jar
Rubber	8	1	#5 Single-hole, Sulfur Free
Stainless Steel	9	1	2" O.D. Planchet

N. Y. State Department of Health

Div. of Env. Health Services
Bur. of Air Poll. Control Services

Fig. 19-1. Lead Peroxide Candle and Assembly

G. L.   June 1961

18. Spatula, 4-inch blade.

19. Razor blade or sharp knife.

20. Glass stirring rods.

21. Rubber policeman.

22. Crucible tongs, long handled.

23. Wash bottle, glass or polyethylene.

24. Tongs, long handled.

V. Reagents

1. Ethyl alcohol, 95%.

2. Gum tragacanth, U.S.P.

3. Lead peroxide (lead dioxide) PbO_2, ACS.
   a. A sufficient quantity should be obtained at one time so that uniform results will be more likely over a long period of testing.

4. Sodium carbonate, anhydrous, ACS.

5. Hydrochloric acid, concentrated, ACS.
   a. Dilute to 50% strength with distilled water.

6. Barium chloride, $BaCl_2.2H_2O$, ACS.

7. Silver nitrate, ACS.

8. Nitric acid, concentrated, ACS.

9. Medium-fiber, acid-washed, purified asbestos.

VI. Preparation of Reagents

1. Gum tragacanth mucilage. Disperse 2 grams of gum tragacanth in 10 ml. of 95% ethyl alcohol, and then add at one time, while stirring, 190 ml. of distilled water.

   a. Upon standing, the mucilage loses its gel-like consistency and becomes watery. It is best to use mucilage which is not more than one month old.

2. Barium chloride solution. Dissolve 100 grams of $BaCl_2.2H_2O$ in one liter of distilled water. Filter through a hard finish filter paper before use. (One ml. of this reagent is capable of precipitating approximately 40 milligrams of SO_4 ion.)

3. Silver nitrate—nitric acid solution. Dissolve 8.5 grams of $AgNO_3$ and 0.5 ml. of concentrated HNO_3 in 500 ml. of distilled water.

4. Asbestos cream. Add 15 grams of acid-washed, medium-fiber purified asbestos to 1 liter of distilled water. Remove the fine material from the asbestos before use by repeated decantations. Add sufficient distilled water to bring the asbestos sus-

pension back to approximately 1-liter volume. Save the fine asbestos suspension.

VII. Preparation of the Asbestos Filter Mat

1. Prepare an asbestos filter mat in a Gooch crucible by using a suitable suction apparatus, such as

 a. The recommended procedure for preparation of the filter mat is as follows: Insert the Gooch funnel in the neck of the filter flask and set a Gooch crucible in the funnel. Start a gentle suction with the vacuum. Pour the asbestos suspension into the funnel so that, when strong light is viewed through the asbestos mat formed in the bottom, a diffuse light can be seen but not the outlines of the individual holes. Disconnect the suction from the filter flask, invert the crucible, and then apply gentle suction to just dislodge the mat. Remove the mat with tweezers or tongs, and remove all loose asbestos fibers from the Gooch crucible. Turn the mat upside down and return it carefully to the bottom of the Gooch crucible. Apply suction to the filter flask. Add more of the fine asbestos suspension so as to overlay the mat with asbestos. Wash the mat with warm distilled water.

Wash several times with hot distilled water and dry at 103°C for 4 hours. Cool the crucible in a disiccator and weigh to the nearest 0.1 milligram.

VIII. Preparation of Candle

The candle is actually a glass tube or test tube with a gauze wrapping on which a pasty mixture of lead peroxide and the gum mucilage has been spread evenly. The resulting product for exposure is not a candle; it merely resembles one vaguely.

Application of gauze to the tube can be made easier if a 1-hole rubber stopper is placed in each end of the tube, or in the open end of the test-tube if used. A wood dowel, slightly smaller in diameter than the stopper holes, can then be passed through them to provide horizontal support for the tube while the gauze and paste mixture are applied to it.

Cut a 16¼″ length of the 4″ gauze, and place four turns around the glass tube. The gauze is actually 9.8 centimeters wide, and if not stretched the wrapping will be this width. Hold the gauze in place with gum mucilage. Measure the width of the gauze wrapping and, if other

than 9.8 cm, adjust it as necessary. Store the wrapped tube in a closed glass jar until just before application of lead peroxide paste.

Prepare the lead peroxide paste by placing 8 grams of lead peroxide (PbO_2) on a clock glass and mix it with 6 milliliters of freshly prepared gum mucilage to obtain a mixture of workable consistency. Return the gauze-wrapped glass tube to the horizontal holder, and apply the entire paste mixture immediately and evenly to the gauze with a spatual, being careful not to go beyond the edges of the gauze. When completed, the width of the applied paste should be 9.8 cm. Any paste mixture which falls off during application should be caught on a clock glass and re-applied.

The prepared candle should be placed in a large desiccating chamber until the surface gloss disappears. Do not dry so excessively as to cause checking and flaking of the paste coating. Place the completed candle in a 16-oz. olive jar for storage and transportation to the sampling site, being careful to keep the coated gauze from touching the glass. An assembly such as in Fig. 19-1 can be used.

IX. Sampling Procedure

1. Construct a shelter for the candle using aluminum pie plates as indicated in Fig. 19-2.
2. Mount shelter on a suitable pipe stand by means of a floor flange fastened to the bottom of the shelter. The pipe stand should support the shelter about 3 to 4 feet above the surrounding surface.
3. Place stand and shelter in a safe location on the roof of your school, keeping well away from the chimney and other obstructions.
4. Place the candle in the shelter; keep it vertical by slipping the jar cover under a sheet metal. If the assembly of Fig. 19-1 is not used; the glass tube may be held upright by placing it on a rubber stopper screwed to the floor of the shelter. Be careful that the aluminum plates do scrape against the coating of lead peroxide.
5. Record the date exposure starts.
6. Leave the candle in the shelter for 30 days ± 4 days. (The tolerance on duration of exposure is allowed because of weekends and holidays.)
7. Remove the exposed candle and place it gently in the olive jar for transportation to the laboratory.
8. Record the date exposure is ended.

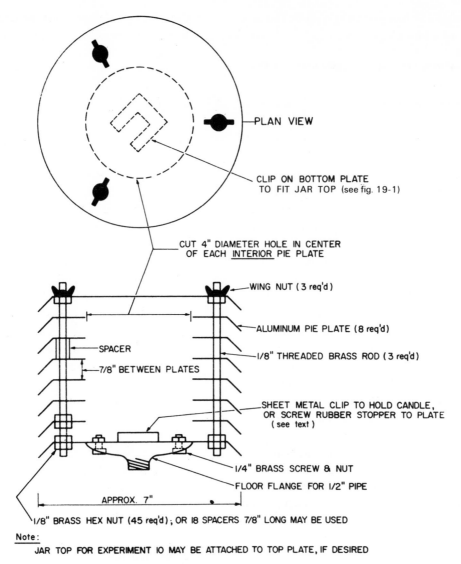

PLAN VIEW

CLIP ON BOTTOM PLATE
TO FIT JAR TOP (see fig. 19-1)

CUT 4" DIAMETER HOLE IN CENTER
OF EACH INTERIOR PIE PLATE

WING NUT (3 req'd)

ALUMINUM PIE PLATE (8 req'd)

SPACER

1/8" THREADED BRASS ROD (3 req'd)

7/8" BETWEEN PLATES

SHEET METAL CLIP TO HOLD CANDLE,
OR SCREW RUBBER STOPPER TO PLATE
(see text)

1/4" BRASS SCREW & NUT

FLOOR FLANGE FOR 1/2" PIPE

APPROX. 7"

1/8" BRASS HEX NUT (45 req'd); OR 18 SPACERS 7/8" LONG MAY BE USED

Note:
JAR TOP FOR EXPERIMENT 10 MAY BE ATTACHED TO TOP PLATE, IF DESIRED

Fig. 19-2. SHELTER FOR LEAD PEROXIDE CANDLE

X. Laboratory Determination

1. Strip off gauze and exposed paste from the glass tube, using a razor blade, sharp knife, or scissors. Place gauze and paste in a 400 ml. beaker. Do the stripping job over the beaker so that any of the exposed paste breaking loose will be caught. Use a policeman and distilled water to remove any exposed paste adhering to the glass tube.

2. Add 5 grams of anhydrous sodium carbonate and 125 to 150 ml. of distilled water. Add more distilled water, if necessary, to completely cover the coated gauze. Stir to dissolve the sodium carbonate.

3. Allow to stand, stirring occasionally, for at least *3 hours* and simmer for *½ hour,* keeping the volume nearly constant by addition of distilled water. Guard against violent bumping.

****(At these points, students may pause until the following day.)

4. Filter the mixture through Whatman #40 filter paper, retaining the gauze in the beaker. Wash the gauze in the beaker several times with small amounts of warm distilled water, adding each washing to the filter paper. Wash and scrape the sides of the beaker, and pour all washings onto the filter. Wash the material on the filter paper until liquid coming from the tip of the funnel is no longer alkaline to litmus paper. (Total filtrate will usually be more than 500 ml.)

5. Re-filter the filtrate through a Gooch crucible.****

6. Cautiously acidify the filtrate with 1:1 HCl (1 part concentrated HCl in 1 part distilled water) to a pH of 3.5 to 4.0. Care should be taken to prevent loss of sample by foaming, especially as the point of neutralization is approached.

7. Heat the solution to boiling and, while stirring gently, slowly add 5 ml. of warm 10% barium chloride solution. Simmer for 30 minutes and digest on a steam bath for 2 hours, maintaining the volume at a minimum of 250 ml. by adding distilled water.****

8. If the volume of liquid is excessive, continue heating until the volume is no more than 500 ml. Remove the beaker of liquid and precipitate and allow it to stand overnight with a cover glass on the top of the beaker.****

9. Adjust the pH of the mixture to 3.5 to 4.0, if necessary.****

10. Weigh the Gooch crucible, containing the asbestos mat to the nearest 0.0001 gram, or 0.1 milligram.

11. Filter the mixture through the tared Gooch crucible. Wash beaker and precipitate on mat with warm distilled water until washings are chloride-free, as indicated by small volumes tested with silver nitrate-nitric acid solution.****

12. As a precaution, treat the filtrate with a second 5 ml. of 10% barium chloride. Set aside overnight to determine whether all sulfate has been precipitated. If precipitation occurs again, repeat steps 7 through 11.****

13. Dry the Gooch crucible with precipitate in an oven at 103°C for 4 hours. Cool in a desiccator and weigh to the nearest 0.0001 gram, or 0.1 milligram.

14. The additional weight is barium sulfate ($BaSO_4$). (Note: The instructor may wish to have several students do the weighing to determine the magnitude of error to be expected.)

XI. Computations

Results are reported in milligrams of sulfate ion per square centimeter per 30 days.

1. Circumference of coated surface equals 10.7 cm.* Area of exposed surface equals 104.86 sq. cm. if the paste was confined to the 9.8 cm. width of gauze.

2. Computation is as follows:

    a. Molecular weight of $BaSO_4$ = 137.36 + 32.06 + 64.00 = 233.42

    b. Molecular weight of $SO_4^=$ = 32.06 + 64.00 = 96.06

    c. Grams of $SO_4^=$ per gram of $BaSO_4$ = 96.06/233.42 = 0.4115

    d. 1 gm. = 1000 mg.

    e. mg. $SO_4^=/cm.^2/30$ days = (grams $BaSO_4$ × 0.4115 × 1000 × 30)/(104.86 × days exposed)

> *This is the circumference measured when using the technique of the Division of Laboratories and Research, New York State Department of Health. In all instances, actual average circumference should be determined by making several measurements.

XII. Records

Keep exact, legible records of all measurements and computations.

XIII. Reference

1. Tentative Method for Sulfur Dioxide Analysis by Lead Peroxide Cylinder; Division of Laboratories and Research, New York State Department of Health; July 13, 1965.

XIV. Prepared by Donald C. Hunter

EXPERIMENT NO. 20

Detection and Measurement of Atmospheric Carbon Monoxide

I. Object

To demonstrate a simple procedure for the measurement of carbon monoxide in the atmosphere.

II. Suitability and Usefulness

1. Can be used to make quantitative measurements of carbon monoxide within the ranges that are considered to have physiological effects on man and animals.

2. Can be used qualitatively to detect emission sources.

III. Theory and Background

Carbon monoxide (CO) is a colorless, odorless gas that is formed by the incomplete combustion of carbonaceous materials. When carbon containing materials such as coal, wool, oil, gas, etc. are burned under normal conditions and with sufficient air, carbon combines with oxygen in the air to form harmless carbon dioxide:

$$C + O_2 \rightarrow CO_2$$

If insufficient air is present, or if the flames are allowed to contact cold surfaces, incomplete combustion results and carbon monoxide is formed:

$$2C + O_2 \rightarrow 2CO$$

Carbon monoxide is combustible, and can be burned with more air to form carbon dioxide.

$$2CO + O_2 \rightarrow 2CO_2$$

At sufficiently high concentrations, carbon monoxide is toxic to man and animals. The toxic effects are caused by the affinity of hemoglobin in the blood for carbon monoxide. The normal function of hemoglobin is to carry oxygen from the lungs to the body tissue. The affinity of hemoglobin for carbon monoxide is over 200 times that for oxygen, and when it is combined with carbon monoxide, it cannot perform its function of carrying oxygen to the body tissues.

As an indication of dangerous concentration levels, the American Conference of Government Industrial Hygienists has established a limit of 50 parts per million (0.005%) average for an 8 hour working day exposure. For continuous exposure some state air pollution authorities have suggested ranges of 5 to 30 parts per million.* For short

exposure periods of up to an hour, concentrations of less than 500 parts per million are said to have little or no physiological effect. Hemoglobin in the blood rapidly regains its capacity to carry oxygen when the air supply is free of carbon monoxide.

The principal sources of carbon monoxide atmospheric pollution are automobile exhausts and incomplete combustion of fuels used for industrial and domestic heating. Studies conducted by the U. S. Department of Health, Education and Welfare for the January, 1967 New York-New Jersey Interstate Air Pollution Abatement Conference indicated that 95% of the carbon monoxide in the air came from automobile exhaust gases and the remaining 5% from industrial and other sources. Federal regulations limit the carbon monoxide content of exhaust gases from 1968 model automobiles to 1.5% maximum.

In confined spaces, especially in the home, dangerous levels of carbon monoxide can come from improperly operating space heaters, hot water heaters and cooking stoves. It is also interesting to learn that the smoke from cigarettes contains 200–400 parts per million of carbon monoxide.

IV. Testing and Measurement

1. *Method*—The National Bureau of Standards has developed a simple method for measuring carbon monoxide in the atmosphere. Samples of air are aspirated through small glass tubes filled with silica gel, on which has been deposited a solution of palladium sulfate and ammonium molybdate. When carbon monoxide in the air comes in contact with this reagent, the pale yellow color of the reagent is converted to a series of

---

*The Environmental Protection Agency has established the following standards for carbon monoxide (*Federal Register,* April 30, 1971):

(a) 9 ppm maximum 8-hour concentration not to be exceeded more than once per year;

(b) 35 ppm maximum 1-hour concentration not to be exceeded more than once per year.

green to blue green colors. The color and shade developed is a direct indication of the proportion of carbon monoxide in the air sample.

2. *Equipment*

    1. Glass tubes filled with silica gel which has been treated with the reagent and sealed on both ends.

    2. A rubber aspirator bulb of 100 ml. capacity.

    3. Standardized color comparison charts relating reacted reagent color to the percent of carbon monoxide in the air sample.

Note: A convenient test kit containing all of the above items and directions for use may be obtained from the Mine Safety Appliance Company, 201 North Braddock Avenue, Pittsburgh, Pennsylvania under Catalogue No. 08-47133 at a cost of about $45.

3. *Directions*

If a test kit similar to the Mine Safety Appliance Company kit is used, break the capillary seals from the ends of a glass reagent tube. Insert the tube in the tester and hold the open end of the reagent tube in the suspected atmosphere. Squeeze the aspirator bulb 1, 2 or 5 times and compare the color developed in the reagent tube with the standard color chart. Carbon monoxide concentrations in the range of 10–1000 parts per million (0.001 to 0.10%) may be determined with this test kit

A rapid qualitative test for carbon monoxide can be made by holding the open end of the tester near the exhaust pipe of an operating automobile engine.

A single squeeze of the aspirator bulb should be enough to develop a green color in the reagent tube.

The color reaction in the reagent tube can also be produced by aspirating smoke from a burning cigarette through the tester.

V. References

1. Frank A. Patty, "Industrial Hygiene and Toxicology," 2nd Ed., Interscience Publishers, New York, 1963.

2. M. Shepard, "A Preliminary Report on the N.B.S. Colorimetric Indicating Gel from the Rapid Determination of Small Amounts of Carbon Monoxide" National Bureau of Standards, June 29, 1946.

3. M. Shepard, Analytical Chemistry, 19, 77 (1947).

4. Magill, Holden and Ackley, "Air Pollution Handbook," McGraw-Hill Book Company, New York, 1956.

5. N. Irving Sax, "Dangerous Properties of Industrial Materials" Reinhold Publishing Company, New York, 1957.

6. "Threshold Limit Values for 1967" American Conference of Governmental Industrial Hygienists, 1014 Broadway, Cincinnati, Ohio.

7. Air Pollution Experiments—High School Edition; Cooperative Extension Service, College of Agriculture and Environmental Science, Rutgers—The State University, New Brunswick, New Jersey 08903; 1967.

VI. Prepared by Russell E. Thurn

EXPERIMENT NO. 21

Determination of Sulfur Dioxide Concentration in Combustion Gases (Peroxide Method)

I. Object

1. To determine the sulfur dioxide concentration in combustion gases by the hydrogen peroxide method.

II. Suitability and Usefulness

1. Demonstrates absorption of gases in easily prepared solutions.

2. Teaches the cleaning of gas samples filtration, the control of gas flow by the limiting orifice, and one method of calibrating a vacuum pump.

3. Provides practice in titrating technique.

4. Makes students aware of, corrections needed for presence of water vapor in gas volumes measured.

III. Theory and Background

Sulfur compounds are present in fossil fuels, especially coal and oil. Such fuels may contain 0.2% to 5% sulfur. During combustion, the sulfur combines with oxygen in the combustion air to form gaseous sulfur dioxide, which may result in deleterious effects to man, animals, vegetation and many materials.

Sulfur dioxide (SO_2) is extremely irritating to the respiratory passages of man and animals, usually severely aggravating symptoms of bronchitis, asthma and other respiratory illnesses. Its effects have been reported more severe when the gas is accompanied by particulate matter. If high concentrations, such as 100% SO_2, are inhaled, the results may be fatal.

The gas enters vegetation foliage through the leaf stomata. The effect may be a yellowing, browning, or reddening of the leaf areas between the veins. Alfalfa, which has its stomata open at night as well as during the day, gets a double dose and is considered one of our most susceptible plants.

Sulfur dioxide may oxidize in the atmosphere to form sulfur trioxide (SO_3), which then combines with water vapor (or rain) to form sulfuric acid (H_2SO_4). Sulfur trioxide or sulfuric acid may react with metal oxides in the air to form metal sulfates. All of these compounds may give the atmosphere a blue hazy appearance, reducing visi-

bility. The sulfuric acid may coalesce into small droplets to create a fine mist, eventually becoming heavy enough to settle onto the first surface that will retain them. Sulfur dioxide may dissolve in water vapor or rain to form sulfurous acid (H_2SO_3), a slightly active "hypothetical" acid never obtained separate from water.

Iron, steel, and stone are attacked. If an iron or steel surface is wet, acid mist falling on it forms an acid solution in contact with the metal, accelerating a series of electrochemical reactions ending in the product we recognize as rust. Sulfuric acid reacts with the calcium carbonate of marble and other stone to form slightly soluble calcium sulfate. That is why inscriptions on many old gravestones and monuments are difficult to read.

In addition to these harmful effects, every pound of SO_2 allowed to escape into the atmosphere represents an irretrievable loss of a half pound of elemental sulfur. (Can you explain the reason for the weight difference?) It has been estimated that during 1967 about 32 million tons of SO_2 were emitted to the atmosphere in the United States, of which about 72%, or 23 million tons, were from stationary combustion sources, such as power generating plants. These 23 million tons represent 11.5 million tons of sulfur lost forever. During the same year, the United States had to mine 7.8 million tons of sulfur which could have been left in the earth for future generations if processes had been available to recover and recycle the SO_2 before it escaped.

The hydrogen peroxide analytical method has been used for many years to determine the concentration of SO_2 in the atmosphere. In general, this method consistshof absorbing SO_2 in hydrogen peroxide solution to form sulfuric acid, which is then titrated to neutrality with sodium hydroxide solution. The principal disadvantage of the method is the interference from acidic and basic gases or particulates which may be present in the gas sampled. Strongly acidic compounds give high results for SO_2, while strong bases give low results.

Urban atmospheric concentrations of SO_2 may range from 0.01 to 0.3 part per million parts of air (ppm) by volume. Concentrations of SO_2 in combustion gases are much higher, and may range from 1,000 to 3,000 ppm. By using absorbing and titrating solutions of suitable concentrations and by adjusting the total volume of gas sampled, the method analyzes the more concentrated gases. A glass fiber filter in the sampling line is used to remove solid particles and any droplets of sulfuric acid. Moisture traps remove water vapor from the sample and protect the gas flow measuring device from the absorbing solutions. A limiting orifice in the line will provide uniform rate of gas flow during the sampling period. Crushed ice in the tray under the first two moisture traps cools the combustion gases to a convenient temperature and condenses water vapor from them.

IV. Equipment

1. Vacuum pump of about 2.0 liters per minute capacity. (A pump with greater capacity may be used.)

2. Limiting orifice, having a critical velocity rating such that it will permit constant flow of about 0.75 liter per minute with a pump rated at 2.0 liters per minute. (Available from Gelman Instrument Co., Ann Arbor, Mich. 48106.)

3. Wet test meter to measure the volume of gas passing through the absorbing solution. One manufacturer is Precision Scientific Co., Chicago, Ill. (While a wet test meter should not be required when a limiting orifice is used, its use is recommended so that students can compare volume measurements by the two methods.)

4. Midget impingers (3 required, two of which are fitted with fritted bubblers).

5. Filter (in-line type) fitted with a glass fiber filter disc. (Gelman Instrument Co.)

6. Stainless steel tubing (¼-inch I.D.) for sampling probe.

7. Glass or Teflon tubing (¼-inch I.D.) from probe past impingers (plastic and rubber tubing will absorb SO_2 and should not be used). Plastic or rubber tubing may be used from the impingers to the pump. (Tubing must be sufficiently rigid to avoid collapse under vacuum.)

8. Erlenmeyer flasks (500 cc.)—3 required as moisture traps and gas coolers.

9. Burette.

10. Ring stand and clamp to hold burette.

11. Rack to hold impingers.

12. Watch or clock.

13. Ice trays and crushed ice to cool gases in the first two moisture traps.

14. A ½-inch diameter sampling hole in the school furnace smoke pipe at the horizontal diameter near its entrance to the chimney. Provision should be made for plugging the sampling hole when it is not in use.

15. Rubber stoppers, sulfur-free.

V. Reagents

1. Hydrogen peroxide, 3% solution. Prepare by diluting 100 ml of 30% hydrogen peroxide to 1.0 liter with distilled water in a volumetric flask. (*Note:* 30% H_2O_2 is very corrosive to the skin. Flush immediately with water.)

2. Sodium hydroxide, 0.02 molar solution.

    a. Prepare a molar solution by dissolving 40 grams of NaOH in distilled water and diluting to a volume of 1.0 liter with distilled water in a volumetric flask.

    b. Dilute 20 ml of the molar solution to 1.0 liter with distilled water to make a 0.02 molar solution. (One liter of this solution will contain 0.8 gram of NaOH.)

3. Mixed indicator solution—dissolve 0.3 gram of brom-cresol green and 0.2 gram of methyl red in 500 ml of methyl alcohol.

VI. Procedure

1. Ask your chemistry teacher to arrange to have a ½-inch diameter hole drilled at the horizontal diameter of your school furnace smoke pipe near its entrance to the chimney, and to have a removable cap or plug made so that the hole can be closed when not in use.

2. Assemble the sampling apparatus illustrated in Fig. 21-1 and set it on a table near the sampling hole.

3. Insert the stainless steel probe in the sampling hole so that you will be sampling combustion gases from about the center line of the smoke pipe.

    (Try out the apparatus with distilled water in the impingers to make certain that bubbling will not be so violent that solution will be drawn into the wet test meter. This will also purge air from the sampling train and fill it with the gas to be sampled.) Fill the trays under the first two flasks with crushed ice to cool the combustion gases.

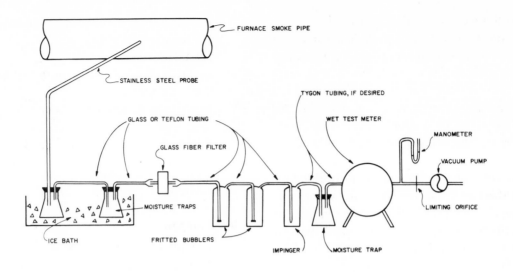

FIG. 21-1

SAMPLING APPARATUS FOR PEROXIDE DETERMINATION OF SO$_2$ IN COMBUSTION GASES.

4. Add about 5 drops of the mixed indicator solution to about 75 ml of the 3% hydrogen peroxide absorbing solution. Then titrate it with 0.02 molar NaOH solution from the burette until the red color disappears and a fluorescent green endpoint appears. (This assures that the absorbing solution is neutral before sampling is started.)

5. Add 20 ml of this green solution to each of the three impingers in the sampling train, and replace the stoppers.

6. Record the wet test meter reading.

7. Start the vacuum pump and record the time to the nearest minute.

8. Continue to sample for about 15 minutes, noting in which impingers the absorbing solution color changes the most as SO$_2$ is absorbed. (The least color change should occur in the third impinger.)

9. Stop the vacuum pump, and record the time and the wet test meter reading.

10. Remove the probe from the smoke pipe, cover or plug the sampling hole, and remove the impinger flasks from the sampling train.

11. Titrate the solution in each impinger with the 0.02 molar NaOH solution to the same fluorescent green endpoint. (Titration may be postponed until the next day if desired.) Keep a record of the volume (ml) of 0.02 molar NaOH solution used for each impinger.

12. Determine the total volume of 0.02 molar

NaOH solution consumed in titrating the solution in the three impinger flasks. Do not include that used before sampling was started. (The total 0.02 molar NaOH solution used after sampling will represent a measure of the H$_2$SO$_4$ produced and of the volume of SO$_2$ absorbed by the hydrogen peroxide solution, as described in "VIII Computations".)

Note: If a wet test meter is not available to measure gas flow, the total flow may be estimated quite accurately as follows:

1. After assembling the sampling train, attach the end of the probe to the upper end of a 6-ft. length of glass tubing supported vertically.

2. Use 20 ml of distilled water in each impinger.

3. Place a dish of soapy water below the glass tube. After starting the vacuum pump, raise the level of soapy water until bubbles are drawn up into the tube.

4. After the inside surface of the tube has become wet, time the 6-foot travel of a single bubble up the tube with a stop watch.

5. Repeat, timing the travel of several individual bubbles.

6. Determine the average time for a bubble to travel 6 feet. Determine the inside diameter of the glass tubing. Convert distances to the proper metric units and time to minutes. Then determine flow rate as follows:

$$\frac{\text{Inside area of tube} \times \text{distance traveled}}{\text{Average time of travel}} =$$

$$\text{Liters per min. (average)}$$

7. Remove the measuring tube. Insert the probe in the smoke pipe. Empty the impinger flasks, add 20 ml of the green solution to each as described previously, and proceed with sampling. Assume that flow rate during the sampling is the average determined in step 6.

VII. Reactions

1. When SO_2 is bubbled through H_2O_2, the following chemical reaction occurs:

$$SO_2 + H_2O_2 = H_2SO_4$$

2. When the resulting sulfuric acid is titrated with NaOH solution, the reaction is as follows:

$$2NaOH + H_2SO_4 = Na_2SO_4 + 2H_2O$$

VIII. Computations

The titrating solution was 0.02 molar NaOH. A 1.0 molar solution contains the molecular weight of the solute in grams per liter of solution.

Since the molecular weight of NaOH is 40 (22.997 + 16 + 1.008), 40 grams of NaOH dissolved in sufficient distilled water to make a solution of 1.0 liter in volume will comprise a 1.0 molar solution. Then a 0.02 molar solution will contain 0.8 (or 40 × 0.02) gram per liter. Since there are 1,000 milliliters per liter and 1,000 milligrams per gram, the 0.02 molar solution will also contain 0.8 mg of NaOH per ml.

In titrating the sample to neutrality, you used y ml of 0.02 molar NaOH. Since each ml of 0.02 molar NaOH solution contains 0.8 mg of NaOH, titration consumed 0.8y mg of NaOH.

We can now write the equation for the reaction and determine the quantity of sulfuric acid neutralized by a simple proportion between weights and molecular weights:

$$\begin{matrix} 0.8y \text{ mg} & w \text{ mg} \\ 2NaOH + H_2SO_4 & = Na_2SO_4 + 2H_2O \\ 80 & 98 \end{matrix}$$

$$0.8y{:}w = 80{:}98, \text{ or } 0.8y{:}80 = w{:}98$$

$$w = \frac{(0.8y)(98)}{80} =$$

$$0.98y \text{ mg of } H_2SO_4 \text{ neutralized,}$$

or

$$\frac{(0.98y)(64)}{(98)} =$$

$$0.64y \text{ mg, or } (0.64 \times 10^{-3})y \text{ gram,}$$

$$\text{of } SO_2 \text{ in } H_2SO_4 \text{ neutralized.}$$

(*Note:* By similar reasoning we can also determine the amount of SO_2 absorbed by considering the amount of NaOH consumed and the amount of Na_2SO_4 produced in the neutralization reaction.)

Realizing that the molecular weight of a gas in grams at 0°C and 760 mm Hg occupies 22.4 liters, we can convert weight of SO_2 sampled to volume.

$$(0.64 \times 10^{-3})(y)\frac{(22.4)}{(64)} =$$

$$(22.4 \times 10^{-5})y \text{ liters of } SO_2$$

Liters of SO_2 in the gas mixture sampled will then be 22.4×10^{-5} multiplied by number of milliliters of 0.02 molar NaOH solution used.

Note: If desired, the value of y can be inserted at any point in the foregoing computations.)

If volume of gases sampled was measured in cubic feet, we can convert to liters as follows:

$$ft^3 \times 28.32 = \text{liters of gas measured}$$

1. Liters of dry gas measured by the rotameter or wet test meter = volume (in liters) measured minus the liters of water vapor contained in it.

Whenever a gas is bubbled through or collected over an aqueous solution, it becomes saturated with water vapor according to the temperature to which the system was subjected (in this case the air temperature within the room where you sampled and measured the gas). Let's assume you bubbled the furnace gas through the H_2O_2 solution in a room having an air temperature of 20°C. From a table of vapor pressures of water or from a table of the properties of saturated steam, you will find that water vapor at that temperature exerts a pressure of 17.5 mm of Hg. According to Dalton's Law of Partial Pressures, the total pressure on a mixture of gases is equal to the *sum* of the pressures each gas would exert on the walls of the container if it alone were so contained. Since your apparatus was under vacuum from the pump, total pressure on the gases measured was that indicated by the barometer (let's assume it was 745 mm of Hg) minus the amount of vacuum indicated by the manometer (assume 5 mm of Hg), or 740 mm of Hg. Then the pressure on the dry gas must have been $740 - 17.5 = 722.5$ mm Hg.

$$\text{or, } V_1 = V_m \times \frac{722.5}{740} =$$
$$0.9764\, V_m \text{ at } 20°C \text{ and } 740 \text{ mm Hg,}$$

where V_m is the volume measured and V_1 is the volume of dry gas only.

In other words, at 20°C (293°K), 722.5/740 × 100 = 97.64% of the volume of gas as measured was dry; the remaining 2.36% was water vapor. Compute from the pressures the % of the total volume measured which was water vapor. Is your answer 2.36%?

2. Liters of SO_2 per million liters of dry gas (ppm) at 0°C, 760 mm Hg.

The total volume of dry gas sampled will be the volume measured as determined in (1) plus the volume of SO_2 absorbed. Since we determined the volume of SO_2 absorbed as $(22.4 \times 10^{-5})y$ liters at 0°C and 760 mm Hg, we have to compute the remaining volume of dry gas measured at the same conditions. Applying Boyle's and Charles' Laws,

$$\frac{P_1 V_1}{T_1} = \frac{P_2 V_2}{T_2}$$

$$V_2 = V_1 \times \frac{P_1 T_2}{P_2 T_1} = V_1 \times \frac{740}{760} \times \frac{273}{293} =$$
$$0.908\, V_1 \text{ liters of dry gas}$$

measured, referred to 0°C and 760 mm Hg. Let's call this V_{DG}

Total dry gas sampled = $V_{DG} + (22.4 \times 10^{-5})y$.

ppm of SO_2 in dry gas sampled = $[(22.4 \times 10^{-5})y]/[V_{DG} + (22.4 \times 10^{-5})y] \times 10^6$.

3. Concentration of SO_2 as ppm of total gas sampled at smokepipe conditions.

As you drew the hot gases from the smokepipe, we shall assume that all water vapor contained in them was condensed to liquid in the two cold moisture traps. By determining the weight of the

condensed water vapor and the temperature within the smokepipe, the total volume of gases sampled can be computed.

Let's assume that you have weighed the water in the two traps and found a weight of 10 grams, and that you have inserted a thermometer in the smokepipe and found its temperature to be 300°F (148.9°C). Referring again to the table of properties of saturated steam, you will find that the water vapor exerts a pressure of 3,465 mm of Hg and has a volume of 0.4035 liter per gram at that temperature. Therefore, the gases sampled contained 4.035 liters of water vapor.

To avoid adding apples to pears, we must convert this volume of water vapor to the same temperature and pressure we used in computing volume of dry gas sampled (0°C, 760 mm Hg).

Volume of water vapor at 0°C, 760 mm Hg =

$$4.035 \times \frac{3465}{760} \times \frac{273}{422} = 11.9 \text{ liters.}$$

Representing the volume of water vapor at standard conditions by V_w and adding it to the denominator of the final equation in (2), we have ppm of SO_2 in total gas sampled = liters of SO_2/ total liters of gas sampled × 10^6 = $[(22.4 \times 10^{-5})y]/[V_w + V_{DG} + (22.4 \times 10^{-5})y] \times 10^6$.

You now have an expression of concentration (ppm by volume) of SO_2 in total gas sampled. It is independent of changes in temerature and pressure. Try it with two squares drawn on a sheet of paper. Then increase or decrease their areas by various temperature and pressure ratios. Note that the ratio of the "gas" square to the "total air" square does not change. Volumes react in the same manner.

4. Compute by how much the concentration of SO_2 would have been in error if you had omitted the corrections for water vapor.

IX. Reproducibility

To determine whether this method will give reproducible results, another student set up an identical sampling train so that the two determinations can be performed at the same time in parallel.

X. Adaptability

This experiment has been written from laboratory work done on a simulated stack gas, using pressure cylinders of 100% SO_2 and air. If it does not work as expected on actual combustion gas, the student should not be discouraged because the adult world is full of blank walls and apparent dead ends. Instead, he should look for possible means of modifying the experiment, such as by changing the amount of gas sampled or the concentration of the solutions.

Caution: Students should work only with actual combustion gases, *and should avoid use of 100% SO₂.*

XI. Records

Keep complete and neat records of
1. Solution preparation.
2. Sampling time.
3. Volume of titrating solution consumed.
4. Volume of gas measured.
5. Barometric pressure
6. Vacuum on apparatus.
7. Temperature of room where gas was measured.
8. Weight of water vapor condensed.
9. Temperature in smokepipe.
10. Concentration of SO_2 found.
11. Unusual observations

XII. Recovery and Recycling of SO₂

If little or no SO_2 was absorbed in the third impinger, you did an acceptable job of recovering SO_2 from the gases sampled. Half of the weight of SO_2 recovered was elemental sulfur. As dilute H_2SO_4, the recovered product would need only to be concentrated by evaporation for direct use as sulfuric acid. While far from an economical recovery process on a commercial scale, it does show that the job can be done. Several processes are being tried on power plant stack gases by which it is hoped high recovery efficiency can be achieved economically.

One process developed recently for recovery of low concentrations of SO_2 from combustion gases involves adsorption of the SO_2 on granular activated carbon by passing the stack or furnace gases at 200 to 300°F through a bed of the carbon. In addition to adsorbing the SO_2, the activated carbon acts as a catalyst to combine the SO_2 with oxygen in the gases to form SO_3. Water vapor then hydrolyzes the SO_3 to H_2SO_4, which is held on the activated carbon until removed. (Formation of H_2SO_4 produces considerable heat.)

A Japanese process involves regenerating the activated carbon by washing it with water to produce a dilute or weak sulfuric acid solution. In one American process, the carbon loaded with H_2SO_4 is treated with hydrogen sulfide gas (H_2S) to produce elemental sulfur, according to the following equation: $3H_2S + H_2SO_4 \rightarrow 4S + 4H_2O$; the sulfur is then vaporized and condensed to regenerate the carbon and to put the sulfur in salable form.

After determining the SO_2 concentration of the furnace gas, you may want to consider inserting the activated carbon adsorber, used in Experiment No. 28, between the smoke pipe and the moisture traps and noting whether concentration of SO_2 in the gas measured is diminished. After washing the carbon with distilled water, you can also determine the amount of sulfur dioxide recovered by titrating an aliquot of the weak acid with sodium hydroxide solution of known concentration. Or, you may wish to pass H_2S gas through the adsorber (under a ventilating hood) and note whether the distinctive yellow color of elemental sulfur can be observed on the carbon granules. (Remember, you will need 3 mols of H_2S for each mol of H_2SO_4 on the carbon, or 3 gram-molecular weights of H_2S for each gram-molecular weight of H_2SO_4.)

XIII. References

1. M. B. Jacobs, The Chemical Analysis of Air Pollutants; Interscience Publishers, Inc., 1960.
2. Seymour Hochheiser, Methods of Measuring and Monitoring Atmospheric Sulfur Dioxide; U.S. Department H.E.W., U.S.P.H.S. Publication 999-AP-6, 1964.
3. H. G. Deming, General Chemistry; John Wiley & Sons, 1923.
4. H. A. Lange, Handbook of Chemistry; Handbook Publishers, Inc., 1934.
5. F. J. Ball, S. L. Torrence, and A. J. Repik, Dry Fluidized Activated Carbon Processes for Stack SO_2 Recovery as Sulfur; J. Air Pollution Control Association, January 1972

XIV. Prepared by Donald C. Hunter, Laboratory work by William Colver

EXPERIMENT NO. 22

Analysis of Sulfur Dioxide in Combustion Gases (Iodometric Titration Method)

I. Object

1. To measure the concentration of sulfur dioxide in actual combustion gases from a furnace burning coal or oil, using the iodometric titration method.

II. Suitability and Usefulness

1. Good as a demonstration project for special science fair displays.

2. Demonstrates a method of sampling which includes concomitant titration, eliminating the necessity of removing the absorbed sample to the laboratory for titration later.

3. Automatically limits sampling duration to the time required for a particular color change to take place in a fixed volume of absorbing solution.

III. Theory and Background

The determination of sulfur dioxide concentration in combustion gases by the "peroxide" method is described in Experiment No. 21. In that experiment you removed the absorbed sample from the sampling train and returned it to the laboratory for titration to determine the quantity of SO_2 absorbed from the combustion gases.

This experiment, involving the iodometric method, makes titration a part of the sampling procedure. The method was originally developed by the Monsanto Company for the analysis of SO_2 in sulfuric acid manufacturing plants. By changing the concentration of the absorbing solution, it has been adapted to gas mixtures such as may be experienced in the combustion gases of a school furnace burning oil or coal. For industrial use, the method is lower in cost because it eliminates a separate laboratory titration.

Sampling and analysis involve bubbling the stack gas containing SO_2 through a solution containing a known quantity of iodine. The SO_2 reduces the iodine according to the following equation:

$$SO_2 + I_2 + 2H_2O = 2I^- + SO_4^= + 4H^+.$$

The iodine solution contains a small amount of a standard starch solution which produces a blue color. When sufficient SO_2 has been absorbed to reduce all the iodine the blue color disappears. (In this experiment the student starts with a faint blue color, goes to a darker blue, and then returns to the original faint blue.)

Concentration is determined as parts of SO_2 per million parts of gases sampled (ppm) by volume. The volume of SO_2 required to complete the reduction process is computed and the volume of the remaining gas sampled is determined by a measuring burette and leveling bottle. Corrections are made for presence of water vapor in the gases sampled and measured.

IV. Equipment

1. Aspirator, or leveling, bottle—250-ml capacity.

2. Gas measuring burette—100 to 200-ml capacity, with upper stopcock.

3. Ring-stand, with clamp, to hold burette.

4. Three-way stopcock.

5. Rubber aspirator bulb, single valve.

6. Gas washing bottle—250-ml capacity.

7. Filter (in-line type) fitted with glass fiber filter disc.

8. Erlenmeyer flasks—500-ml capacity; required as moisture traps, gas coolers, and for titrations.

9. Tray for crushed ice to cool gases in moisture traps.

10. Stainless steel tubing (¼-inch I.D.) for sampling probe.

11. Teflon tubing (¼-inch I.D.), from first moisture trap to gas washing bottle.

12. Tygon or rubber tubing (¼-inch I.D.), from gas washing bottle to leveling bottle.

13. Rubber stoppers, sulfur-free.

14. Beakers, graduated cylinders, volumetric flask, amber glass bottles, pipettes—for reagents.

V. Reagents

1. Stock Iodine Solution—0.1 Normal

Dissolve 12.692 grams of resublimed iodine which has been weighed carefully, in 25 ml of a distilled water solution containing 15 grams of iodate-free potassium iodide (KI). (The KI must be present as a saturated solution before the iodine will dissolve. It may help to grind the iodine in the KI solution with mortar and pestle.) Dilute with distilled water to the 1,000-ml mark in a volumetric flask. This solution should be stored in an amber

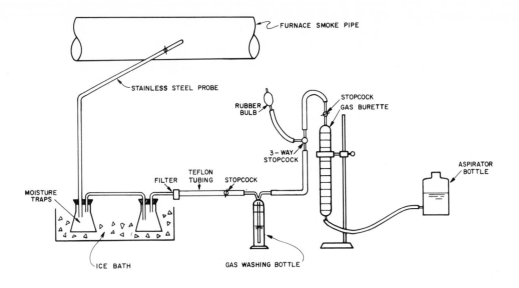

FIG. 22-1

MEASUREMENT OF SO₂ IN A FURNACE SMOKE PIPE (IODOMETRIC METHOD)

glass bottle, refrigerated, and standardized with standard 0.1 Normal sodium thiosulfate solution *on the day of use.*

Note: We use ½ of the molecular weight of iodine to form a Normal solution because each iodine atom has a valence change of 1 when combining with hydrogen and thus has a hydrogen equivalent of 1.

2. Sodium Thiosulfate Solution—0.1 Normal

Sodium thiosulfate is combined with five molecules of water of crystallization. Its formula is $Na_2S_2O_3 \cdot 5H_2O$. Because it contains water which cannot be separated before the salt is in solution, the molecular weight of the water must be included in determining the quantity needed for a 0.1 Normal solution.

A 1.0 Normal solution will contain 248.192 grams per liter (45.994 + 64.12 + 48.00 + 90.078). For a 0.1 Normal solution, weigh 24.8192 grams, dissolve it in 100 ml of distilled water, and dilute it with distilled water to one liter in a volumetric flask. (Standardization of the 0.1 N sodium thiosulfate solution by the chemistry teacher is recommended.)

3. 0.002 Normal Iodine Working Solution

After standardization of the 0.1 Normal iodine solution with 0.1 Normal sodium thiosulfate solution, as described later, dilute 20 ml of the 0.1 Normal iodine solution with distilled water to one liter in a volumetric flask.

4. Starch Indicator Solution

Add 1.0 gram of soluble starch to 50 ml of distilled water, boil briefly, cool, and add 0.5 gram of KI.

VI. Standardization of 0.1 Normal Iodine Solution

(*Note:* This step may be omitted if weighing and preparation of the 0.1 Normal iodine solution has been done carefully.)

To standardize the 0.1 N iodine solution pipette 50 ml into a 500-ml Erlenmeyer flask. Add 1 ml of concentrated HCl and let the flask stand in an ice bath until all fumes are absorbed. Titrate with 0.1 N sodium thiosulfate solution, swirling the contents of the flask continuously. When the solution becomes straw colored, add a few drops of fresh starch solution. Continue the titration until 0.02 ml (a half-drop) of the sodium thiosulfate removes the blue color. Check your work for accuracy by repeating the standardization. Computations involved will be found in VIII Chemistry.

VII. Procedure for Sampling and Analysis

1. Assemble the apparatus, as illustrated in Fig. 22-1, on a small table placed near the smoke pipe of the school furnace.

2. Close the stopcock at the probe, open the one at the entrance to the gas washing bottle, disconnect the tubing from the entrance to the washing bottle,

and apply a light vacuum to the tubing at that point to remove all air from the apparatus between the probe and the gas washing bottle.

3. Close the stopcock near the washing bottle, insert the probe in the hole in the smoke pipe. (The end of the probe should be at about the centerline of the smoke pipe.) Disconnect the vacuum pump.

4. Slowly open the stopcock at the probe so that the apparatus just evacuated will fill with combustion gases.

5. Keeping the stopcock at the other end of the tubing closed, connect the tubing to the inlet to the gas washing bottle.

6. Fill the gas washing bottle about ⅔ full of distilled water. Add 5 ml of starch solution and one or two drops of the 0.002 N iodine solution to produce a faint blue color, which should be carefully noted for future reference.

7. Add 10 ml of the 0.002 N iodine solution to the gas washing bottle.

8. Fill the leveling bottle with distilled water. Open both the stopcock at the top of the burette and the 3-way stopcock. Raise the leveling bottle to transfer water to the burette and expel all air from it through the aspirator bulb. (Add more distilled water to the leveling bottle, if necessary, to keep the water level above its hose connection.)

9. Then raise or lower the leveling bottle as necessary to fill the burette to the zero mark with water. (When measuring the level in the burette, always bring the water level in the bottle and in the burette to the same elevation.) Close the stopcock at the top of the burette, and then close the 3-way stopcock.

10. Flush the remainder of the sample line by means of the rubber aspirator bulb. (Gas being flushed out will be expelled through the bulb.)

11. Raise the leveling bottle until the water level in the burette is again at the zero mark. Open the 3-way stopcock and then open the burette stopcock. Open the stopcock at the entrance to the gas washing bottle.

12. Lower the leveling bottle to create vacuum, or negative pressure, above the water in the burette and draw gas slowly from the smoke pipe through the gas washing bottle. Swirl the reagent in the washing bottle while bubbling. Continue bubbling until the solution in the washing bottle decolorizes to the same faint blue shade you noted in step 6.

13. Close the burette stopcock and read the volume of water displaced after bringing the water level in the burette and in the leveling bottle to the same elevation.

If the concentration of SO_2 is such that more than one buretteful of gas must be measured before the solution in the washing bottle reaches the desired shade of blue, bubbling should be stopped at a point near burette capacity and the volume of gas measured and recorded. Then repeat steps 11 through 13 as many times as necessary to reduce all of the iodine in the 10-ml addition, as indicated by the same faint blue shade of the solution. Determine and record the total gas measured by the burette for all passes.

VIII. Chemistry

1. Standardization of Iodine Solution with 0.1 Normal Sodium Thiosulfate solution.

Sodium thiosulfate solution of known normality can be used in determining the normality of iodine solution because of the reaction which takes place according to the following equation:

$$2Na_2S_2O_3 + I_2 = 2NaI + Na_2S_4O_6$$

We know the following facts:

a. Our 0.1 Normal solution of sodium thiosulfate contains 15.811 g of dry salt, $Na_2S_2O_3$, per liter, or 0.015811 g per ml.

b. The molecular weight of the two molecules of $Na_2S_2O_3 = 316.22$.

c. The molecular weight of the iodine is 253.84.

d. A 0.1 Normal solution of iodine should contain 12.692 g per liter, or 0.012692 g per ml.

We can now computer the grams of iodine, equivalent to one ml. of the thiosulfate solution:

$$\begin{array}{ccc} 0.015811 \text{ g/ml} \times & g & \\ 2Na_2S_2O_3 & + \quad I_2 & = 2NaI + Na_2S_4O_6 \\ 316.22 & 253.84 & \end{array}$$

$$0.15811 : x = 3.16.22 : 253.84$$

$$x = \frac{(.015811)(253.84)}{316.22} = 0.012692 \text{ g,}$$

which is also the quantity of iodine in one ml. of 0.1 Normal iodine solution. Therefore, 1 ml. of 0.1 Normal sodium thiosulfate solution is equivalent to 1 ml. of 0.1 Normal iodine solution. From this, we can say that the volume of sodium thiosulfate solution times its normality is equal to the volume of iodine solution times its normality.

(1) Normality I_2 × ml. I_2 = Normality thiosulfate × ml. thiosulfate

(2) Normality I_2 =

$$\frac{\text{Normality thiosulfate} \times \text{ml thiosulfate}}{\text{ml } I_2}$$

If normality of the iodine solution is not 0.1 ± 0.005, we can correct the stock solution by either concentration or dilution. Since dilution with distilled water is obviously the simpler correction to make, it is advisable, in making up the stock 0.1 Normal iodine solution, to try for a concentration slightly greater than 0.1 Normal if there is any question about accuracy of weighing the ingredients. The volume of distilled water to be added (in liters) to one liter of solution will be the difference between the normality found and the normality desired multiplied by 10 when normality is in 10ths. (Example: If Normality found should be 0.2 Normal, we would add 1 liter of water to bring the concentration to 0.1 Normal. If it is found to be 0.12, we would add 0.2 liter of water to make the correction.)

Or we can compute the dilution as follows:
Final total volume of solution × desired Normality = Existing volume × Normality found

Final total volume =

$$\frac{\text{Existing volume} \times \text{Normality found}}{\text{desired Normality}}$$

Volume of distilled water to be added for proper dilution is then the difference between "final total volume" and "existing volume".

2. Reduction of Iodine by SO_2 in Combustion Gases

Before starting to sample, you added 10 ml of 0.002 Normal iodine solution to the gas washing bottle, after first adding 5 ml. of starch solution and one or two drops of iodine solution to produce a faint blue color. You then bubbled combustion gases through the iodine until all 10 ml. of 0.002 Normal iodine solution were reduced by SO_2 to HI as shown by the same faint blue color you had at the beginning. This reducing reaction is illustrated by the following equation:

$$SO_2 + I_2 + 2H_2O = 2HI + H_2SO_4.$$

The 0.002 Normal iodine solution contains 0.25384 g of I_2 per liter, or 0.25384 mg per ml, and you consumed 10 ml of the iodine solution

containing 2.5384 mg of I_2. You can now compute the amount of SO_2 required to reduce 10 ml of 0.002 Normal iodine solution:

$$\underset{64.06}{\overset{x\text{mg}}{SO_2}} + \underset{253.84}{\overset{2.5384\text{ mg}}{I_2}} + 2H_2O = 2HI + H_2SO_4$$

$x : 2.5384 = 64.06 : 253.84$

$$x = \frac{(2.5384)(64.06)}{253.84} =$$

$0.6406 \text{ mg of } SO_2 = 0.0006406 \text{ g of } SO_2.$

At standard conditions, 64.06 g of SO_2 occupy 22.4 l. Therefore, 0.0006406 g will occupy $0.0006406 \times \frac{22.4}{64.06} = 22.4 \times 10^{-5}$ l. $= 10^{-2}$ ml.

Note: It is not necessary to adjust the iodine solution to exactly 0.1 Normality to perform the experiment. Such adjustment is merely a convenience to chemists doing routine analyses.

Let's assume you found the iodine solution 0.12 Normal after titration with standard 0.1 Normal sodium thiosulfate. That is the same as saying it was 1.2 times as concentrated as a 0.1 Normal solution. Your dilution of 20 ml to 1 liter will be 0.0024 Normal instead of 0.002 Normal, and each ml will contain 0.30461 mg of iodine instead of 0.25384 mg. Then the 10 ml in the gas washing bottle will contain 3.0461 mg of iodine which will require 0.76872 mg of SO_2 to complete its reduction. There will be no difference in the final result for concentration of SO_2 in the combustion gases because you will have sampled 1.2 times as much gas to get 1.2 times as much SO_2.

IX. Computations

Concentrations of contaminating gases are frequently expressed in volumes per million volumes of air or other carrier gas. This is commonly called parts per million by volume, or ppm by volume.

It is assumed that the contaminating gas and the other gases sampled follow the perfect gas laws, and expand or contract according to Boyle's and Charles' Laws. Therefore we can assume that the expression of concentration in ppm by volume is independent of changes in temperature and pressure. (Example: A concentration of 2 ppm at 0°C and 760 mm Hg is also 2 ppm at any other combination of temperature and pressure.)

However, volume of SO_2 gas adsorbed, or used

in reducing the iodine in the gas washing bottle, and the volume of combustion gases measured in the burette must both be put on the same basis of temperature and pressure before we relate one to the other.

Under "Chemistry," we computed the volume of SO_2 absorbed at standard conditions (0°C and 760 mm Hg) when we converted from grams of SO_2 to liters of SO_2. Therefore, we must correct the volume of gas measured in the burette to the same temperature and pressure.

According to Boyle's and Charles' laws,

$$P_1 V_1 / T_1 = P_2 V_2 / T_2$$
$$V_2 = V_1 \times (P_1 T_2 / P_2 T_1)$$

where

V_1 = volume of gases as measured in the burette.
T_1 = room temperature, °Kelvin (°C + 273).
P_1 = barometric pressure (mm of Hg) minus the aqueous tension (vapor pressure of water at T_1 in mm of Hg). This correction is necessary because the gases measured were bubbled through an aqueous solution and are saturated with water vapor. Water vapor, like a gas, tends to expand, and accordingly relieves the dry gas of a part of the atmospheric pressure it would otherwise have to bear. In other words, Dalton's Law of Partial Pressures applies as it did in the preceding Experiment No. 21.
V_2 = Volume at standard conditions (0°C and 760 mm Hg).
T_2 = standard temperature, 273°K (0°C).
P_2 = standard pressure, 760 mm Hg.

Volume of SO_2 can now be related to total volume of combustion gases sampled to determine concentration of SO_2 in them. Total volume of dry gas sampled will be the sum of the gas volume measured by the burette (V_2) plus the volume of SO_2 which remained behind in the wash bottle.

Note: If your iodine solution was not exactly 0.1 Normal, you will have a volume of SO_2 other than 0.224 ml.

To determine concentration of SO_2 as ppm parts of total gas sampled, correct for water vapor at smokepipe conditions as described in preceding Experiment No. 21.

X. Adaptability

This experiment has been written from laboratory work done with a simulated furnace gas, using room air and a pressure cylinder of 100% SO_2. If it should not work as expected, the student should look for possible means of modifying the experiment, such as by changing the concentration of the solution or the rate of gas flow.

XI. References

1. Atmospheric Emissions from Sulfuric Acid Manufacturing Processes; U.S. Public Health Service Publication No. 999-AP-13, 1965.
2. M. B. Jacobs, The Chemical Analysis of Air Pollutants; Interscience Publishers, Inc., 1960.
3. Morris Katz, Air Pollution, Vol. II, 2nd ed; Academic Press, Inc., 1968.
4. H. G. Deming, General Chemistry; John Wiley and Sons, Inc., 1923.
5. N. A. Lange, Handbook of Chemistry; Handbook Publishers, Inc., 1934.

XII. Prepared by Frederick B. Higgins, Jr.

$$\text{Parts of } SO_2 \text{ per part of dry gas sampled} = \frac{0.224 \text{ ml. of } SO_2}{V_2 \text{ (in ml.)} + 0.224}$$

$$\% SO_2 \text{ (parts per hundred parts of dry gas sampled)} = \frac{0.224}{V_2 \text{ (in ml.)} + 0.224} \times 100$$

$$\text{ppm } SO_2 \text{ (parts per million parts of dry gas sampled)} = \frac{0.224}{V_2 \text{ (in ml.)} + 0.224} \times 1,000,000$$

EXPERIMENT NO. 23

Measuring Atmospheric Turbidity

I. Object

1. To measure atmospheric turbidity by means of a sun photometer.

2. To demonstrate that small particles suspended in the atmosphere reduce visibility by increasing turbidity.

II. Suitability and Usefulness

1. Use of the instrument is simple and requires minimum instruction.

2. Good as a demonstration to show that visibility can be reduced by pollution on a cloudless day.

III. Theory

The visible portion of the sun's radiation, having wavelengths from about 4,000 to 7,000 Angstroms, is called light. When such radiation strikes small particles and droplets in the atmosphere, it is deflected and in so doing strikes other particles and droplets for further deflection. This is called scattering of light, which reduces our ability to see through the atmosphere.

The term atmospheric turbidity is used to describe reduction of the transparency of the atmosphere due to scattering of incoming visible light. We say that visibility is less today than it was yesterday because increase in turbidity has made it impossible for us to see as far as we could yesterday. This experiment will be concerned with measuring by how much turbidity of the atmosphere is increased (visibility reduced) by scattering of incoming visible light.

Measurement of the amount by which the brightness of the incoming solar beam of light is reduced by scattering can be made with the Volz sun photometer. When the instrument is pointed at the sun, light entering a small aperture at the front passes through a filter which transmits a monochromatic beam having a wavelength of about 5,000 Angstroms. This portion of the incoming radiation falls on a photocell whose current output, proportional to the brightness of the beam, is indicated by a microammeter.

The theory of operation of the Volz sun pho-

tometer is based on the assumption that the logarithm of the ratio of the light intensity sensed by the instrument to the intensity of light at the outer edge of the atmosphere is proportional to the atmospheric turbidity. This relationship is expressed mathematically as follows:

$$\log_{10} J/J_0 = -BM$$

where

J = light intensity measured by the observer.

J_0 = light intensity at the outer edge of atmosphere.

B = turbidity coefficient.

M = optical air mass measured by the observer.

To assist in the determination of B, nomographs are available (Figs. 23-4 and 23-5).

IV. Equipment

1. Volz-type sun photometer, such as
   a. Model 019-1 available from Climet Instruments, Inc., Sunnyvale, Calif., or
   b. Built by students (see next experiment in this Manual).

2. Nomograph, traced from scales presented herewith.

3. Straight edge.

V. Procedure

Whether purchased or home-made, the instrument must be calibrated before use to determine its J_0 value to use with one of the nomographs in determining B, the coefficient of turbidity. If purchased, the instrument will have been calibrated by the manufacturer. If home-made, you will need to calibrate your instrument. Even in using a purchased instrument, calibration will be a worthwhile exercise to determine how closely you can duplicate the J_0 value supplied with the instrument.

A. Calibration

Choose a completely clear day with a minimum of haze or turbidity (clouds must be absent). Take the instrument to the top of a mountain, the roof of a high building, or other high elevation. Make several observations throughout the day, as described, from mid-

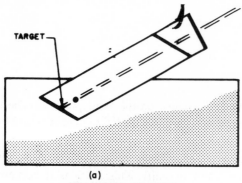

(a)
MEASURING AIR MASS

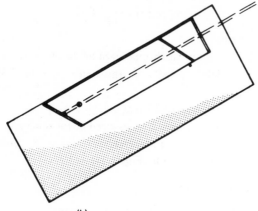

(b)
MEASURING SOLAR INTENSITY

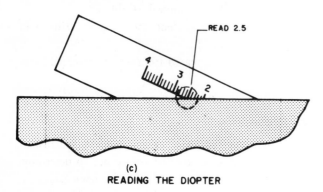

(c)
READING THE DIOPTER

FIG. 23-1 USE OF DIOPTER TO MEASURE AIR MASS

morning until mid-afternoon. Avoid obstructions, such as trees or power poles, which would interfere with the path of the sun's rays to the aperture at the front of the instrument. Readings must be taken out-of-doors —never through a window.

Each observation consists of two readings —(1) air mass (M), which is determined by measuring the angle of the sun's rays to the horizontal; (2) intensity (J) of the monochromatic beam striking the photocell (in microamperes).

The front aperture should always be covered with black tape or a lens cover, except when a measurement of light intensity is being taken.

1. Face the sun while holding the instrument case *level* with the horizontal at waist height, as determined by the bubble in the instrument level.

2. Raise the diopter at the side of the case until the beam of sunlight shining through the two holes at the front falls exactly on the white spot at the rear of the diopter.

3. Read the value of air mass (M) from the diopter scale at the point where the scale intersects the top of the instrument case. Record this value as the first reading for Observation #1. (*Note:* M readings greater than 4.0 occur only when the sun is very close to the horizon.)

4. Lower the diopter to its original position on the side of the case so that it touches the stop.

5. Tilt the front of the case upward until the beam of sunlight again passes through the holes in the diopter and shines on the white dot at the rear. Remove the aperture cover. Read and record the light intensity (J) as indicated by the microammeter.

Note: See Figs. #23-1 and #23-2.

After making observations throughout the day, plot air mass vs. intensity values for each observation on semi-log paper, with air mass on the linear abscissa and intensity on the logarithmic ordinate. Fit a straight line through the plotted points and continue it through the ordinate. The intensity at "zero" air mass is the J_0 calibration value of the instrument.

TYPICAL CALIBRATION DATA FOR SUN PHOTOMETER

AIR MASS (M)	INTENSITY (J)
3.1	38
2.9	40
2.6	43
2.3	45
2.1	47

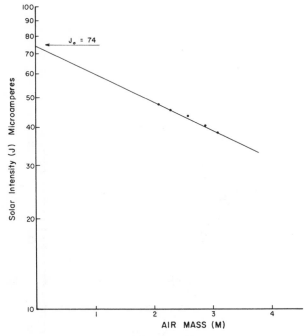

FIG. 23-2 TYPICAL CALIBRATION CURVE

B. Determination of Turbidity Coefficient

1. To determine the turbidity coefficient (B) at *any* location, proceed as described for "Calibration" and obtain readings of air mass (M) and light intensity (J).

2. The turbidity coefficient is read directly from the "B" scale of Nomograph I if atmospheric pressure is 29.92″ ± 1.5″ of mercury. If atmospheric pressure is less than 28.42″ or greater than 31.42″ of mercury, use Nomograph II and computer the turbidity coefficient (B) from the "A" scale reading. (*Note:* Making your own nomographs by exactly tracing those supplied with this experiment is recommended if you build your instrument.)

3. Place the Intensity scale beside the "Δlog J" scale of the nomograph, as illustrated, so that the J_0 calibration value coincides with

the proper seasonal mark near the top of the "Δlog J" scale.

4. Using the straight edge, connect the intensity (microammeter) reading (J) with the air mass (M) reading for the observation.

5. If Nomograph I was used, read the turbidity coefficient (B) at the point where the straight line crosses the "B" scale. If Nomograph II was used, correct the "A" scale reading as follows:

Turbidity coefficient (B) =

$$A - 0.0674\,P/P_0,$$

where

P = actual absolute atmospheric pressure

P_0 = standard absolute atmospheric pressure

Note: When using a ratio of absolute pressures, you can use values for any units of measure, provided you are consistent in the numerator and denominator. Standard absolute atmospheric pressure is 14.7 lbs./in.², 760 mm Hg, 29.92″ Hg, or 1013 millibars at sea level.

VI. Records

Keep neat and complete records of your calibration and turbidity coefficient determinations.

VII. Problem

Try relating turbidity coefficients determined to visibility (the estimated miles you can see through the atmosphere). Is it possible to develop a definite correlation factor to translate turbidity coefficients into visibility in miles?

Visibility is defined as "the greatest distance at which a black object of suitable dimensions can be seen and recognized against the horizon sky" under daylight conditions.

VIII. References

1. R. A. McCormick and D. M. Baulch, The Variation with Height of the Dust Loading over a City as Determined from the Atmospheric Turbidity, APCA Annual Meeting, May 1962.

2. Operating manual; Climet Instruments, Inc., Sunnyvale, California.

3. A. C. Stern, Air Pollution, Vol. II, 2nd Ed.; Academic Press, 1968.

4. Magill, Holden, and Ackley, Air Pollution Handbook; McGraw-Hill, 1956.

5. Handbook of Chemistry and Physics, 40th Ed.; Chemical Rubber Publishing Co., 1958–59.

IX. Prepared by William M. Delaware and David J. Romano

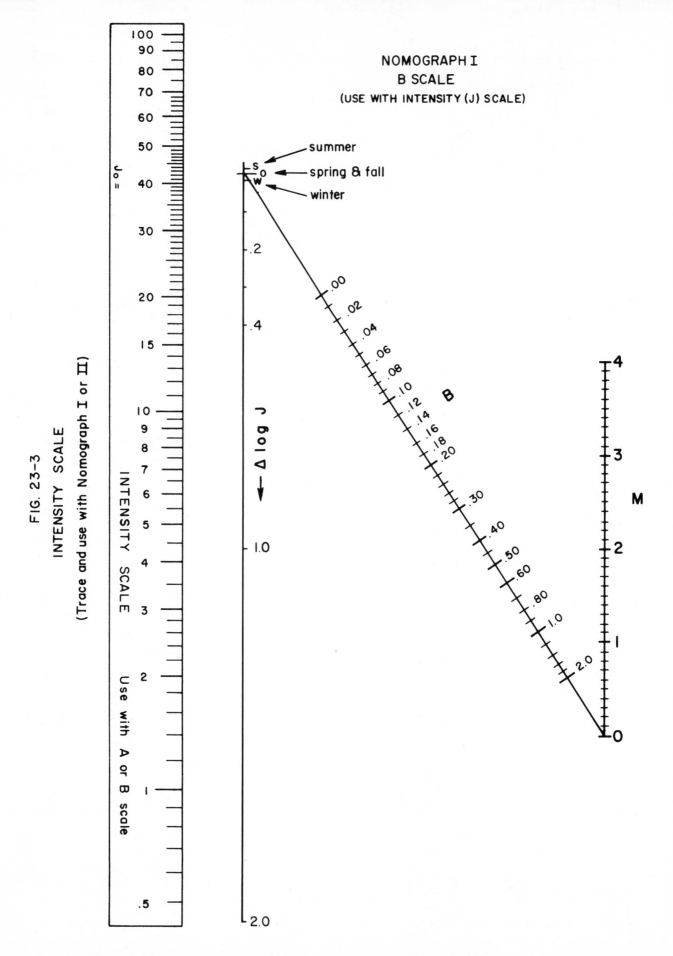

FIG. 23-3
INTENSITY SCALE
(Trace and use with Nomograph I or II)

NOMOGRAPH I
B SCALE
(USE WITH INTENSITY (J) SCALE)

NOMOGRAPH II
A SCALE
(USE WITH INTENSITY (J) SCALE)

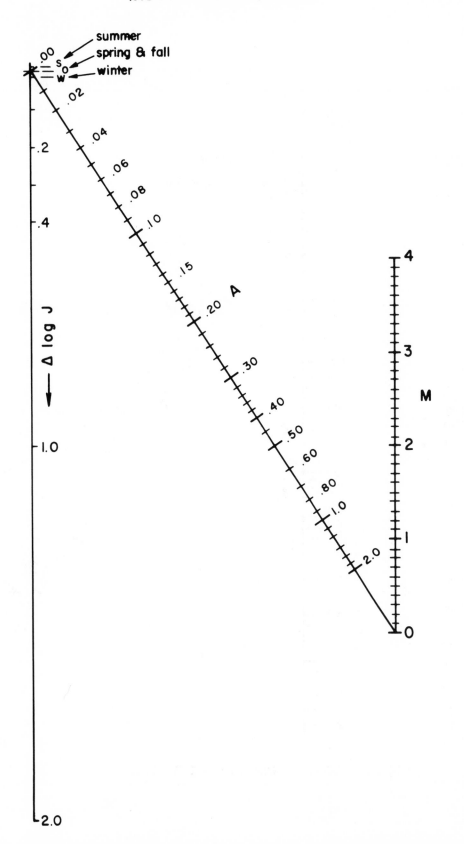

TURBIDITY DIAGRAM
NOMOGRAPH I

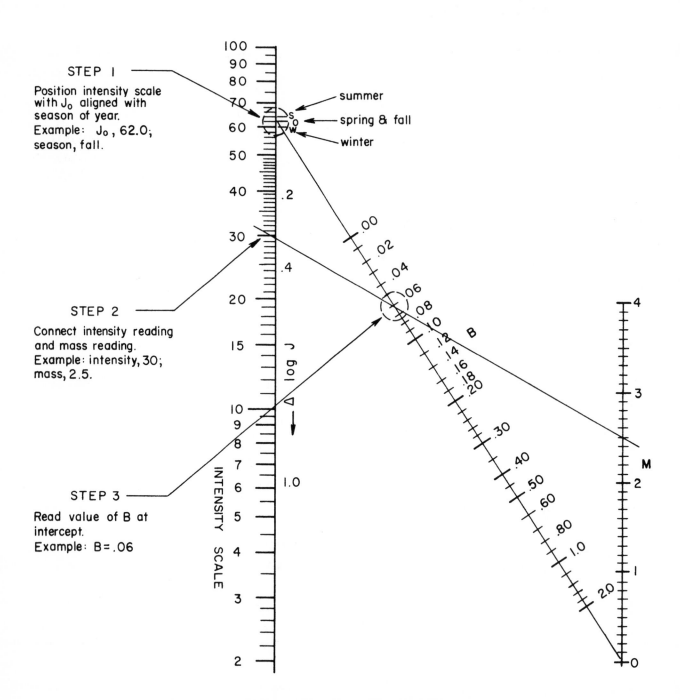

STEP 1

Position intensity scale with J_o aligned with season of year. Example: J_o, 62.0; season, fall.

summer

spring & fall

winter

STEP 2

Connect intensity reading and mass reading. Example: intensity, 30; mass, 2.5.

STEP 3

Read value of B at intercept. Example: B = .06

FIG. 23-6 USING NOMOGRAPH I TO FIND B

EXPERIMENT NO. 24

Construction of a Volz Sun Photometer

I. Object

1. To construct a Volz sun photometer for determination of the coefficient of atmospheric turbidity.

II. Suitability and Usefulness

1. Construction of the instrument gives students a good opportunity to learn how it operates in making measurements for determination of atmospheric turbidity.

2. Building an instrument capable of making actual measurements adds to the student's confidence in his ability.

III. Background

The Volz sun photometer is a relatively simple instrument for measuring the angle of the sun with the horizontal and the intensity of a beam of sunlight, from which a measure of atmospheric turbidity can be determined. It is of simple construction, yet great care must be taken to assure proper dimensions, alignment of parts, and complete sealing of all joints to exclude stray light.

The preceding experiment presented the theory of operation of the instrument. Thus you will appreciate that the beam of light entering the forward aperture must have a clear straight path through the filter to the photocell if an accurate measurement of light intensity is to be made. Likewise, the diopter must have its two holes aligned with the white spot at the rear, and all three must form a straight line parallel with the scale itself if an accurate measure of the sun's angle with the horizontal is to be made. The diopter and nomograph scales must be exact reproductions of those illustrated herewith.

IV. Materials

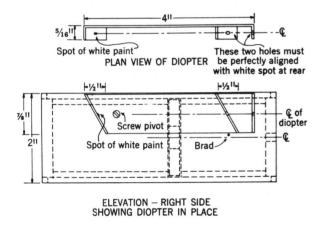

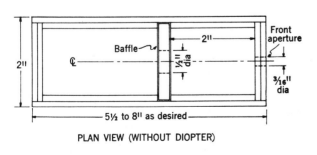

Fig. 24-1 Construction drawing – sun photometer

Item	Approx. Cost, $	Supplier
1. Selenium Solar Cell, output 0.5 v at 0.6 ma, peak spectral response, 5,500 Angstroms	1.25	Lafayette Radio Electronics, Model #276-115, or equivalent
2. Triplett DC Microammeter, Model 120, 0–50 range, 1½″ edgewise	23.00	Triplett Corporation, Bluffton, Ohio
3. Potentiometer, Ohmite Type AB, 5,000 ohms; or equivalent	5.00	Electronic Supply store
4. Kodak Wratten #65 Filter, ½″ square	2.00	Photo supply shop
5. Line level	1.00	Hardware store
6. Diopter	5.00	Machine shop fabrication
7. ½ sq. ft. hardwood, planed if necessary to ¼″ thickness	1.00	Lumber supplier
8. Black paint	Negligible	
9. Small brass wood screws	″	
10. Flat-head wood screw (¼″) and washer		
11. Brad (½″)		
Total cost approx	$35.00 to $40.00	

V. Equipment

Various tools in wood and machine shops.

VI. Procedure

1. The hardwood instrument case with inner baffle should be constructed according to the drawings in Fig. 24-1. Outside dimensions of 5½″ × 2″ × 2″ are suggested for convenience, but may be modified somewhat if desired. All adjoining edges should be rabbeted and must fit tightly to prevent stray light from entering the case. Available lumber will probably have to be planed to the desired ¼″ thickness.

2. Before assembly, the sidewalls, top, and bottom should be routed as shown on the drawings to receive the baffle with a snug fit. The front face of the baffle must be exactly 2 inches from the inside surface of the front end piece.

3. The top should be slotted through as indicated in the photograph so that the level and the microammeter scales can be seen and read easily. Cement the level in place beneath its slot, using an epoxy or other suitable adhesive.

4. The front end piece and the baffle should be drilled on center with a ³⁄₁₆″ diameter aperture in the front piece and a ½″ diameter hole through the baffle. The centers of both holes must be in alignment when the case is assembled.

Fig. 24-3 Bottom of case removed, showing baffle, level, and microammeter in place.

Fig. 24-4 Diopter raised for reading of air mass (M)

5. Install the microammeter in the cover so that its face is visible when the case is assembled. Hold it in place with screws into or through the cover as required. Install the potentiometer at a convenient place in the back piece or in the side behind the baffle.

6. Paint the entire inner surface of the case, including the level, the microammeter, and the potentiometer, with black paint from a small aerosol can. Be sure to paint the inner surface of both holes. (Allow plenty of ventilation when painting, and do not inhale paint vapors.)

7. Cut a piece of the Wratten filter to fit over the ½″ hole and fasten it to the front side of the baffle with electrician's black insulating tape.

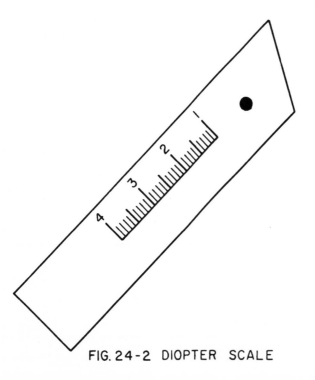

FIG. 24-2 DIOPTER SCALE

8. Center the selenium solar cell over the ½" hole on the rear side of the baffle and fasten it in place similarly. Keep a piece of the black tape over the front aperture at all times when the instrument is not in use.

9. Connect the black wire from the solar cell to the microammeter terminal nearest the zero end of the scale. Connect the red wire to the microammeter terminal nearest the 50 μa end of the scale.

10. Connect the black and red wires from the potentiometer to the microammeter similarly.

11. Fabricate the diopter from $\frac{1}{32}$" brass sheet, or equivalent, as shown in the drawing. Copy the diopter scale exactly from Fig. 24-2 and attach it to the back side of the diopter (see step 12(b) below).

12. Attach the diopter to the right side of the case with a flathead screw and washer so that

a. Its top edge is flush and parallel with the top of the case when the diopter is down against its brad stop.

b. The scale at 1.0 is flush with the top edge of the case when diopter scale is vertical or at right angles to the top of the case.

VII. Prepared by William M. Delaware, Eric M. Holt, and David J. Romano

---

EXPERIMENT NO. 25

Temperature Inversion in a Populated Valley

I. Object

1. To demonstrate development of a temperature inversion in a populated valley during the night.

2. To observe the accumulation of air pollution in the valley during the inversion.

3. To observe dispersion of the air pollution from the valley as the inversion breaks up.

II. Suitability and Usefulness

1. Can be used as an experiment at the junior and senior high school levels.

2. Good as a demonstration project.

3. The experiment illustrates and teaches the effect of temperature on the density of gases.

4. The experiment emphasizes the need for clean air in areas subject to frequent temperature inversions.

III. Theory

Temperature of the atmosphere normally decreases about 5°F with each 1,000 feet of elevation. During the day, the radiant energy of the sun warms the earth, which in turn warms the adjacent layer of air. This warmer air is less dense (has a lower weight per cubic foot) than the air above and rises through the cooler air above. Warm smoke and gases being discharged by smokestacks and chimneys also rise through the cooler air above and are blown away and dispersed by the wind in the upper air.

After sundown the earth's surface cools quickly and in turn cools the layer of air adjacent to the earth. Because of the difference in elevation, the surface air near the top of a hill is colder than surface air near the bottom of the hill. And because a given volume of air becomes heavier as its temperature drops, the cold air near the top of the hill actually flows down the hillside and collects at the bottom under the layer of warmer air directly above it.

If the bottom of the hill is in a valley, this colder air will be flowing down both sides of the valley and will gradually cool the smoke and polluting gases so that they cannot rise through the overlying warmer air. The result is that the pollution continues to collect and become more concentrated in the space where people live near the ground.

The next morning, the rising sun gradually warms the ground, which in turns warms the layer of polluted air adjacent to it. This warm layer of air rises and eventually warms the entire polluted layer until it is able to rise through the warm layer which had been holding it down. A complete overturn of the air, which is called the break-up of the inversion, then occurs.

IV. Equipment

1. Box with V-shape bottom and glass ends. See sketch, Fig. 25-1.

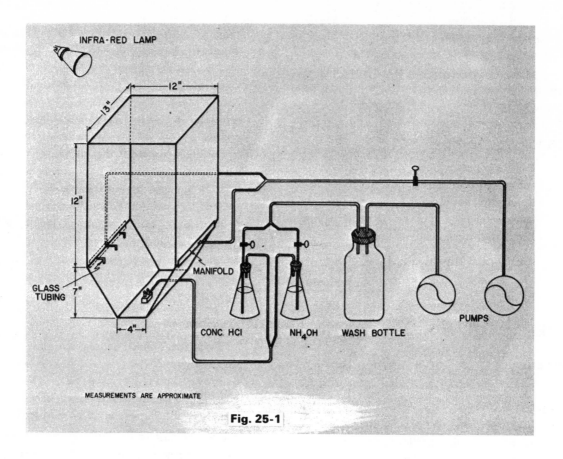

INFRA-RED LAMP

13"

12"

12"

GLASS TUBING

7"

4"

MANIFOLD

CONC. HCl

NH₄OH

WASH BOTTLE

PUMPS

MEASUREMENTS ARE APPROXIMATE

Fig. 25-1

2. Brass, copper, or glass tubes (¼″ × 9″ long) with a 90° bend about three inches from one end. The 3-inch section will represent vertical smoke stacks of factories situated in the valley. The longer section will pass horizontally through the valley wall near the bottom for attachment to a source of simulated smoke.

3. Six short lengths of brass or laboratory glass tubing, each with a 90° bend near one end. These will be placed at the top of the valley walls to direct cold air down the slopes. See sketch.

4. Two small air pumps or rubber aspirator bulbs to propel smoke and cold air.

5. Source of smoke, such as an ammonium chloride generator. The smoke generator can be made from an air pump and two midget impingers, one of which contains ammonium hydroxide and the other of which contains concentrated hydrochloric acid. Adjust the rate of air flow by means of pinch cocks on the air tubing from the pump. See sketch.

6. Rubber or plastic tubing (3/16″ inside diameter) to transport air and smoke from the pumps or aspirators. (Students may find it desirable to use a coil of ¼″ copper tubing packed in dry ice for rapid cooling of air.)

7. Large tray (about 6″ × 12″ × 4″ deep) for crushed ice in which the tubing from the air pump of aspirator will be buried to provide chilled air. Extra tray for possible use in chilling the bottom of the box. Plastic bags filled with crushed ice.

8. Infrared heat lamp, 150 watts.

9. Ring stand and swivel clamp to hold and position the lamp.

V. Procedure

1. Assembly of equipment.

   a. Construct a box with a V-shape bottom and glass ends as illustrated in the accompanying sketch. This simulates a valley and part of the air space above it.

   b. Install two or more smokestacks (¼″ brass, copper, or glass tubing) so that tops of the stacks are about 3 inches above the valley floor. See sketch. Small match boxes can be used to represent factory buildings.

   c. Attach tubing from the smoke generator to the bottom of each stack.

   d. Install the pieces of glass or copper tubing with the 90° bend as illustrated in the sketch. These will direct chilled air down the valley

Fig. 25-2

slopes. Connect these tubes to the air pump by means of long lengths of tubing and suitable plastic manifold connectors. Bury about 8 inches of each tube length in crushed ice. (For more rapid chilling of air, it may be found desirable to use a coil of ¼″ copper tubing packed in dry ice.)

e. Mount the heat lamp on the ring stand by means of a suitable swivel clamp. Adjust it so that, when lighted, its beam will be directed downward through the rear glass wall toward the valley floor at an angle of about 30° from the vertical.

2. Demonstration (Fig. 25-2–25-6 illustrate what happened during one inversion.)

a. Start pumping air through the ammonium chloride smoke generator and note that the smoke rises from the stacks to the top of the box and out of the vent.

b. Fill the tray with crushed ice, and bury about 8 inches of the lengths of the plastic tubes for air supply in the crushed ice. To simulate rapid cooling of the earth's surface after sundown, set the box on a tray of crushed ice and pack a plastic bag of crushed ice against the outside of each valley wall.

c. Start the air pump and regulate the air flow so that cold air flows gently down the slopes of the valley walls.

d. Note the change in shape of the smoke plumes as cold air fills the valley.

e. Continue with smoke and chilled air and note that smoke pollution gradually fills the valley beneath the warmer layer of air.

f. Stop the flow of cold air.

g. Remove the ice from beneath valley floor and from the valley walls.

h. Turn on the infrared heat lamp, beaming it at the valley floor. Observe the plumes and the pollution as the valley floor and the polluted air above it are warmed by the infrared heat rays.

Note: If students desire to actually see cold air flow down the valley walls, repeat step C, using chilled ammonium chloride smoke instead of chilled air.

VI. Record of Observations

1. Students should record their observations as the various steps are performed.

VII. References

1. Experiments for the Science Classroom Based on Air Pollution Problems, State of California Department of Public Health, 2151 Berkeley Way, Berkeley, California 94704, Revised 1962.
2. Course manual "Community Air Pollution," U.S. Public Health Service, Robert A. Taft Sanitary Engineering Center, 4676 Columbia Parkway, Cincinnati, Ohio.

VIII. Key to Drawing and Photographs

Fig. 25-1 Schematic drawing of apparatus.

Fig. 25-2 Photograph showing "colored" cool air flowing down valley walls.

Fig. 25-3 Factory smoke as cool air starts flowing down the valley walls.

Fig. 25-4 Pollution continues to accumulate during the "night."

Fig. 25-5 "Sunrise" starts to warm the "earth"; inversion starts to break up.

Fig. 25-6 Inversion broken; pollution is now warmer than the air above and is rising for complete dispersal.

IX. Prepared by Donald C. Hunter. Experimental Work: Thomas Moran

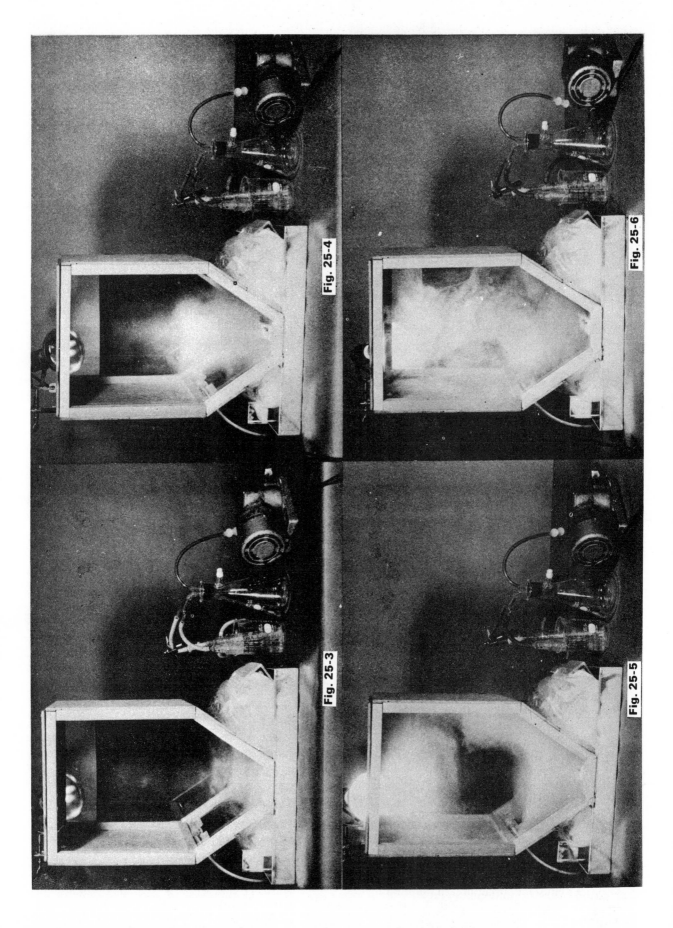

Fig. 25-3

Fig. 25-4

Fig. 25-5

Fig. 25-6

EXPERIMENT NO. 26

The Value of Precipitation in Cleansing the Air

I. Object

1. To determine whether precipitation (rain or snow) washes polluting substances from the air.
2. To measure rainfall and snowfall.
3. To measure specific contaminants which are collected with respect to contaminant concentration, to time, and to amount and intensity of precipitation.

II. Suitability and Usefulness

1. Good as a laboratory experiment, demonstration, or project in a chemistry course.
2. Demonstrates one natural cleansing property of the atmosphere.

III. Theory

Pollution in the form of gases, vapors, fumes and/or particulates enters the atmosphere from a myriad of sources, both natural and man-made. Some of the particles act as nuclei on which water vapor condenses in the cooler upper air and then falls to earth as rain or snow. As rain or snow falls, it can remove other foreign materials from the atmosphere by interception or other mechanical actions and by absorption.

Long before the advent of the automobile and even before the industrial revolution, there was natural and man-made contamination of the atmosphere. Dusts and pollens were picked up by the wind. Campfires and home-heating fireplaces, due to incomplete combustion, contributed their share of particulates and gases. The breaking of surf on waves in the ocean suspends droplets of salt water in the atmosphere. The water in the droplets evaporates to produce salt particles. Such particles can be carried aloft where they act as nuclei on which water vapor condenses.

Emissions from combustion processes, open burning, the internal combustion engine, and many other forms of modern man's activity have substantially increased the atmospheric pollution load above that contributed by nature and the simpler modes of living.

The amount of pollution washed from the atmosphere depends on the concentration of pollution at the time of a storm, the size of droplets, the inten-

sity of the storm, and its duration. The kinds of pollution present which can be washed from the air are almost infinite. However, we shall consider only a few of the more common ones which are known to have health and economic effects.

IV. Collection of Rainfall and Snowfall

A. Equipment
    1. Rain and snow gage (see Figure 26-1).

Note: The collector can be any flat-bottomed, cylindrical container. The measuring tube can be any smaller diameter flat-bottomed, cylindrical tube (a test tube or equivalent) with a diameter approximately $\frac{1}{10}$ the size of the collector. The collector can be mounted on any support stand such as a ring stand. A scale or ruler with relatively small gradations is also necessary.

B. Procedure
    1. Clean the collector and measuring tube thoroughly and rinse with distilled water.
    2. Collect a sample of rainfall or snowfall and record amount collected in inches and the duration of rainfall or snowfall in minutes.

        (a) A ratio of the cross sectional area of the measuring tube to the collector must be calculated and multiplied by the depth measured in the measuring tube to get a true depth of rainfall in inches, relative to the diameter of the collector.

        (b) If snowfall is to be collected, remove the measuring tube and allow the snow to fall directly into the collector. Record the depth of snowfall in inches and the depth of equivalent rainfall, when melted, in inches. (Usually, a relationship of one inch of rain is equivalent to ten inches of snow. Compare your results.)

        (c) A volume of at least 250 ml. of rainfall must be collected in order to run the entire experiment.

V. Determination of Soluble Sulfate

A. Theory
    Sulfur dioxide can be a hazard to human health when in sufficient concentration in the atmosphere. It increases the frequency and intensity of symptoms related to bronchial or other respiratory dis-

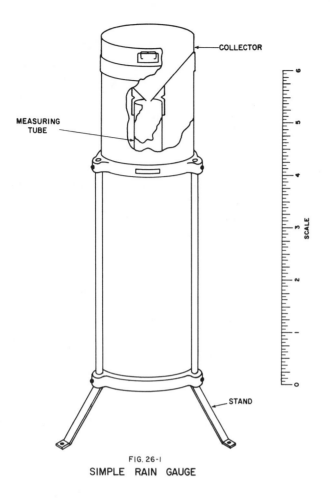

FIG. 26-1
SIMPLE RAIN GAUGE

eases, and has been reported to have its most severe effects when accompanied by particulate matter. It causes chronic injury to certain vegetation. After oxidation to sulfur trioxide and/or hydration to sulfuric acid, it reduces visibility, accelerates corrosion of many metals, and disintegrates masonry and stone.

The following procedure determines the concentration of sulfate ion washed from the air, and present as sulfuric acid and/or soluble sulfate salt.

B. Equipment
    1. Steam bath
    2. Desiccator
    3. Oven equipped with temperature control
    4. Analytical balance
    5. Gooch crucible

C. Reagents
    1. Methyl red indicator: Dissolve 0.1 g methyl red in 7.4 ml. 0.05 N NaOH and dilute to 100 ml. with distilled H_2O.
    2. Hydrochloric acid: Dilute to 50% strength with distilled water.
    3. Barium chloride solution: Dissolve 100 g

of $BaCl_2 \cdot 2H_2O$ in 1 liter of distilled water. Filter through a hard finish filter paper before use. (One ml. of this reagent is capable of precipitating approximately 40 mg. of $SO_4^=$ ion.)

4. Silver nitrate-nitric acid solution: See Section VI, Experiment 19.

5. Surfactant, or wetting agent, such as Ashless Anti-Creep manufactured by Schleicher & Schuell Co., Keene, N. H.

D. Laboratory Procedure
1. Determine the weight of the volume of precipitation collected. (Density of H_2O = 62.4 lb./ft.^{3}.)

2. Precipitation of barium sulfate: Best results in analyzing the sample can be expected if a portion, or aliquot, containing about 50 mg. of sulfate ion is used. Use approximately a 50-ml. aliquot. Dilute this to a 250-ml. volume with distilled water, and make the solution just acidic to methyl red indicator by careful dropwise addition of 50% HCl. (Lower concentrations of sulfate ion may be tolerated if it is impracticable to concentrate the sample to the optimum level, but, in such cases, it is better to fix the total volume at 150 ml.) Heat the solution to boiling and, while stirring gently, add warm barium chloride solution slowly until precipitation appears to be complete; then add about 2 ml. in excess. (If the amount of precipitate is small, add a total of 5 ml. of barium chloride solution.) Digest the precipitate at 80°–90°C, preferably overnight but not less than 2 hours. Maintain the volume at its original magnitude by adding distilled H_2O as required.

3. Prepare an asbestos filter mat as described in Section VII of Experiment 19.

4. Filter the barium sulfate at room temperature through the tared Gooch crucible (containing the asbestos mat), weighed to the nearest 0.0001 gram, or 0.1 milligram. Wash the precipitate with several small portions of warm distilled water until the washings are free of chloride, as indicated by testing with silver nitrate-nitric acid solution. (If a membrane filter is used, add a few drops of the anticreep solution to the suspension before filtering and also to the wash water, to prevent adherence of the precipitate to the holder.) Dry the crucible; filter the precipitate by the

same procedure used in preparing the filter. Cool in a desiccator and weigh to the nearest 0.0001 gram, or 0.1 milligram. The additional weight is barium sulfate.

5. Computation is as follows:

a. Molecular weight of $BaSO_4 = 137.36 + 32.06 + 64.00 = 233.42$

b. Molecular weight of $SO_4^=$ ion $= 32.06 + 64.00 = 98.06$

c. mg. $SO_4^=$ per mg $BaSO_4 = 98.06/233.42 = 0.4115$

d. mg. $SO_4^=$ per ml. of precipitation $=$ (mg $BaSO_4 \times 0.4115$)/ml. of sample used

e. mg. of $SO_4^=$ per liter of precipitation $=$ (mg $BaSO_4 \times 411.5$)/ml. of sample used

f. Knowing the cross-section area of the collector, we can compute the mg. of $SO_4^=$ washed from the air per inch of precipitation.

VI. Particulate Determination

A. Theory

Suspended and settleable particulates are major air pollutants generated from most combustion sources. Particulates in the atmosphere cause reduced visibility, aggravate respiratory diseases, and react with other contaminants to accelerate corrosion and effects on health.

B. Laboratory Procedure

1. From Step D-1 of the Laboratory Procedure of Determination of Soluble Sulfate, record the weight of the volume of precipitation collected.

2. Transfer the precipitate and all visible solid particles to a clean beaker, and proceed with the analytical procedure described in Experiment No. 16 for determination of settleable particulates.

3. From the weight of particulate matter collected, determine the weight of collected particulates per inch of rainfall.

VII. pH Determination

A. Theory

The pH value of a solution represents the hydrogen ion concentration. By definition, pH is the logarithm of the reciprocal of the hydrogen ion concentration. The pH scale extends from O, very acidic, to 14, very alkaline, with pH 7 corresponding to exact neutrality at 25°C.

1. Principle: Several types of electrodes have been suggested for the electrometric determination of pH. Although the hydrogen gas electrode is recognized as the primary standard, the glass electrode in combination with the reference potential provided by saturated calomel electrode is most generally used. The glass system is based on the fact that a change of 1 pH unit produces an electrical change of 59.1 mv at 25°C.

2. Interference: The glass electrode is relatively insensitive to interference from color, turbidity, colloidal matter, free chlorine, oxidants, or reductants, as well as from high saline content, except for a sodium error at high pH. Temperature exerts two significant effects on pH measurements: the electrodes themselves vary in potential, and ionization in the sample varies. The first effect can be compensated by an adjustment which is provided on better commercial instruments. The second effect is inherent in the sample and is taken into consideration by recording both the temperature and the pH of each sample.

B. Equipment

Any commercially available pH meter may be used. Equilibrium, as shown by the absence of drift, should be established between the sample and the electrode system before readings are accepted as final. The student should be on the alert constantly for possible erratic results arising from mechanical or electrical failures—weak batteries, cracked glass electrodes, plugged liquid junction, and fouling of the electrodes with oily or precipitated materials.

C. Preparation of Buffer Solutions

Electrode systems are calibrated against buffer solutions of known pH values. Since buffer solutions may deteriorate because of mold growth or contamination, it may be advisable to prepare them freshly as needed by dissolving dry buffer salts in distilled water. Commercially available buffer tablets or powders of tested quality may also be used. It is good practice to calibrate the electrodes with a buffer having a pH close to that of the samples, so as to minimize any error resulting from nonlinear response of the electrode. In making buffers from solid salts, it is imperative that all of the material be dissolved; otherwise the pH may be incorrect. Polyethylene bottles are preferable for the storage of buffers and samples, although pyrex glassware may be used.

In general, ACS grade chemicals are satisfactory for the preparation of the following buffer solutions:

1. pH 4 buffer solution: Dissolve 10.21 g anhydrous potassium biphthalate, $KHC_8H_4O_4$, in distilled water and dilute to 1,000 ml.

2. pH 7 buffer solution: Dissolve 1.361 g anhydrous potassium dihydrogen phosphate, KH_2PO_4, and 1.420 g anhydrous disodium hydrogen phosphate, Na_2HPO_4, both of which have been dried for 2 hr. at 110° to 130°C. Use distilled water which has been boiled for 15 min. and cooled to room temperature. Dilute to 1,000 ml.

3. pH 9 buffer solution: Dissolve 3.81 g sodium borate decahydrate (borax), $Na_2B_4O_7 \cdot 10H_2O$, in distilled water that has been boiled for 15 min. and cooled to room temperature. Dilute to 1,000 ml.

D. Laboratory Procedure

Because of differences between many makes and models of pH meters available commercially, it is impossible to provide detailed instructions for correct operation of every instrument. In each case, the manufacturer's instructions must be followed. The glass electrode and the calomel electrode should be thoroughly wetted and prepared for use in accordance with instructions given. The instrument can be standardized against a buffer solution with a pH approaching that of the sample. The linearity of electrode response can be checked against at least one additional buffer of a different pH. The readings with the additional buffers will give a rough idea of the limits of accuracy to be expected of the instrument and the technique of operation.

E. Precision and Accuracy

The precision and accuracy attainable with a given pH meter will depend on the type and condition of the instrument used and the technique of standardization and operation. The limits of accuracy under normal conditions are 0.1 pH.

VII. References

1. F. A. Berry, Jr., E. Bollay, and N. R. Beers, "Handbook of Meteorology," McGraw-Hill Book Company, Inc., 1945.

2. A. C. Stern, "Air Pollution," Vol. I, Academic Press, 1968.

3. "Standard Methods for the Examination of Water and Wastewater"; American Public Health Association, Inc.

4. M. B. Jacobs, "The Chemical Analysis of Air Pollutants"; Interscience Publishers, Inc., New York, 1960.

VIII. Prepared by Daniel M. Barolo

EXPERIMENT NO. 27

Reduction of Odors by Potassium Permanganate

I. Object

1. To demonstrate one means by which certain odors can be prevented from polluting the atmosphere.

II. Suitability and Usefulness

1. Excellent as a science demonstration project.
2. The experiment can be expanded, depending on the location of the school, to many types of odor sources.

III. Theory

Many manufacturing, food processing, and disposal operations are the producers of odorous gases or vapors highly irritating and obnoxious to the public. These conditions sometimes become so bad that relations between those responsible for the foul odor and the public deteriorate to the point of a civil suit.

Different remedies are used in different situations to destroy the odor producing substance or to mask the odor with one more pleasant. One means of destroying the odor producing substance is to oxidize it to another less odorous substance. One example of oxidation would be a combining of the odorous substance with oxygen, as in burning or combustion. Another example is illustrated by this experiment.

Potassium permanganate ($KMnO_4$) has long been known as a powerful oxidizing agent. In neutral and mildly alkaline solutions, $KMnO_4$ gains three electrons, liberating 1½ atoms of nascent oxygen, and produces insoluble manganese dioxide. The atoms of nascent oxygen combine with the odorous substances, oxidizing them to less odorous compounds. This alkaline type of reaction is considered best for air pollution applications. It is non-corrosive to most metals and plastics used in industry and it is easily controlled. Also, the manganese dioxide formed has a large surface area, and improves the effectiveness of the potassium permanganate in adsorbing unoxidized and partially oxidized contaminants.

Best results are obtained with the alkalinity of the permanganate solution held at a pH of about 8.5. This can be done by adding a suitable buffer material such as borax, sodium carbonate, or sodium bicarbonate.

With pH above 10, consumption of $KMnO_4$ is excessive; while, with pH far on the acidic side, free permanganic acid is formed which is corrosive to most metals used in industry.

IV. Equipment

1. Oilless gas pump (approximately 2 liters per minute capacity).
2. Pyrex U-tube, packed with Raschig rings or glass beads.
3. Beaker to hold U-tube.
4. Two fritted bubblers, or equivalent.
5. Rotameter or other means of measuring rate of gas flow.
6. Glass or plastic tubing.
7. Stopcocks or pinch cocks.
8. pH indicator.
9. Rubber stoppers for U-tube and bubbler flasks.

V. Reagents

1. Odorous material to be selected by students, perhaps representing local conditions. (Hydrogen sulfide and mercaptans are possibilities.)
2. Potassium permanganate.
3. Buffer material, such as borax, sodium carbonate, or sodium bicarbonate.

VI. Procedure

Assemble the apparatus as illustrated in Fig. 27-1. If fritted discs are not available, students may improvise as required to break up the gas into very small bubbles. (The smaller the bubbles, the greater will be the bubble surface area for contact with the solution for a given volume of gas and the greater will be the efficiency of oxidation.)

Note: If manganese dioxide (MnO_2) formed in the reaction is sufficient to plug the small holes of the fritted bubbler, students may find it necessary to resort to a frit with larger openings or to an impinger.

1. Place the liquid, producing or containing the odorous vapor or gas, in the U-tube so that the Raschig rings or glass beads are thoroughly wetted by it.
2. Place 900 milliliters of 1% $KMnO_4$ solution, buffered to pH 8.5 with borax, sodium carbonate or sodium bicarbonate, in one of the flasks.

Fig. 27-1. Apparatus used in KMnO$_4$ oxidation experiments with air pollutants

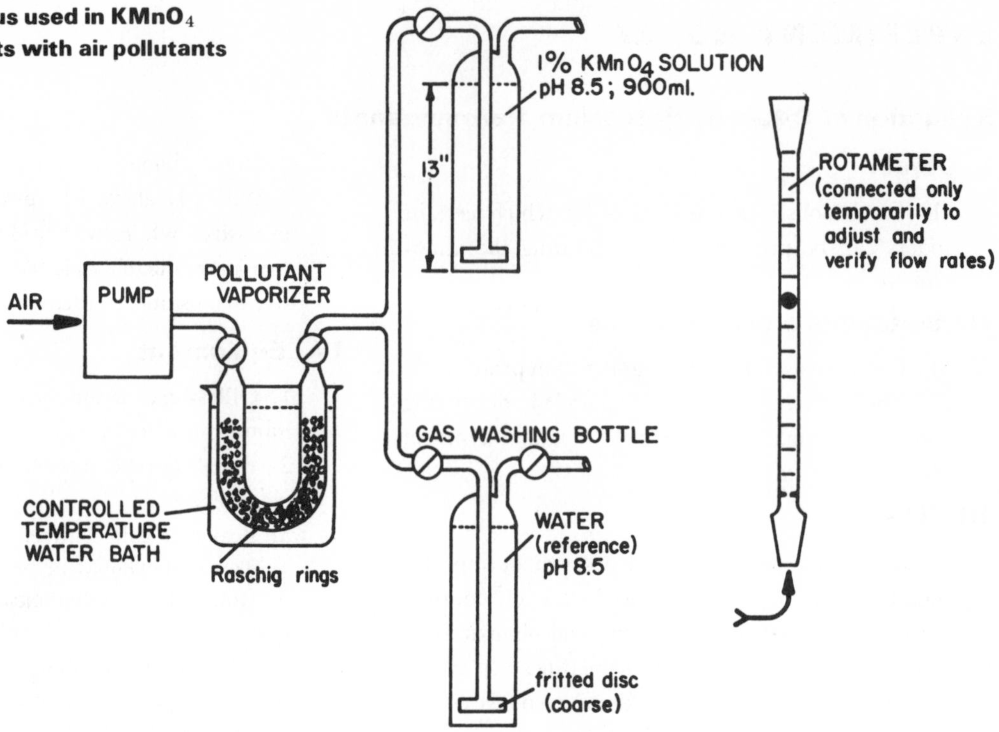

1% KMnO$_4$ SOLUTION
pH 8.5; 900ml.

13"

ROTAMETER (connected only temporarily to adjust and verify flow rates)

AIR PUMP POLLUTANT VAPORIZER

GAS WASHING BOTTLE

CONTROLLED TEMPERATURE WATER BATH

Raschig rings

WATER (reference) pH 8.5

fritted disc (coarse)

3. Place a similar quantity of distilled water, buffered to pH 8.5, in the other bubbler flask.

4. Start the gas pump and adjust the flow rate to 2 liters per minute, passing air through the U-tube. Flow through each bubblers flask will be at the rate of 1 liter per minute. By using water or ice in the beaker, heat or cool the liquid in the U-tube according to its vapor pressure so that the air stream passing through will be loaded to the maximum with the odorous gas or vapor.

Observe and record the nature and intensity of the odor emitted from each bubbler flask.

Do you think the spent solution from a commercial or industrial operation would be sufficiently oxidized by the permanganate to avoid a water pollution complaint if dumped to the sewer?

Note: Students with a rural background, involving cattle feeding operations, may wish to extend the foregoing experiment to a practical application in the destruction of odors in cattle feedlots. The following practice, which has been found most effective, should be carried out under the supervision of the science teacher:

1. Remove manure from feedlots at least three times per year and scarify the ground to promote aerobic bacterial conditions.

2. Follow each scarification with spraying of the ground with a 1% solution of potassium permanganate in water so that each treatment amounts to 20 pounds of KMnO$_4$ per acre. A field spray rig,

if available, can be used.

Other rural students may wish to experiment with destruction of odors common to poultry and hog production, using either the 1% solution or potassium permanganate in crystalline form.

VII. Records

Keep a record of the odorous substances treated and a complete description of your observations. The amount of odor reduction might be estimated.

VIII. References

1. Odor Abatement with Potassium Permanganate Solution, Hans S. Posselt and Arno H. Reidies; I & EC Product Research and Development, March 1965.
2. Potassium Permanganate Offers New Solutions to Air Pollution Control, A. G. Emanuel; Air Engineering, September 1965.
3. Odor Control in Cattle Feed Yards, W. L. Faith; J. Air Pollution Control Association, November 1964.

IX. Prepared by Donald C. Hunter, P.E.

Credit: Fig. 27-1 and part of the foregoing are reprinted from I & EC Product Research and Development, Vol 4, No. 1, March 1965, pages 48 through 50. Copyright 1965 by the American Chemical Society. Reprinted by permission of the copyright owner.

EXPERIMENT NO. 28

Reduction of Odors by Activated Carbon

I. Object

1. To demonstrate a means by which certain odors from closed systems can be prevented from polluting the atmosphere.

II. Suitability and Usefulness

1. Good as a science demonstration project.
2. Teaches the principles of adsorption.
3. Helps students to realize that the public does not need to be annoyed by odors originating in closed systems.

III. Theory and Background

Many gaseous and volatile odorous emissions of industrial processes and food processing plants are considered to be waste products or not economically recoverable, and are permitted to enter the outdoor air for disposal. These odors are annoying to the public, and perhaps represent the waste of products having considerable economic value.

One means of removing odorous gases and vapors from a gas stream is by the principle of adsorption onto solid surfaces. There are several effective adsorbing materials, each having characteristics making it best applicable to individual situations. One of these is activated carbon.

The power of activated carbon to remove odorous gases and vapors from air has been known for many years. One early use was in gas masks during World War I to remove poison gases from the air breathed by soldiers. A fraction of a liter of activated carbon was found capable of reducing the mustard-gas concentration of air, when inhaled at 60 liters per minute (well above human requirements), to less than 1 part per hundred million.

Charcoal is produced from the destructive distillation of wood, coconut and other nut shells, fruit pits, bituminous coal, and petroleum residues. Treatment with live steam, hot air, or hot gases produces the activated product with a porous structure, having a very large surface area per unit of volume or weight. Total surface area is in the order of several hundred thousand square feet per pound. Pore diameter and hardness are determined by the nature of the raw material and the activation process. Hardness is essential to minimize excessive powdering in shipping and handling. Most activated carbon for adsorption of gases ranges in grain size from 4 to 20-mesh (U.S. Sieve Series).

Atoms, molecules, and ions in the solid state are held together by forces which exist throughout a solid and at its surface. Those forces at the surface can bind other molecules which come in contact with the surface or close to it. Any gas, vapor, or liquid will thus adhere to some extent to a solid surface. This phenomenon is known as adsorption. When a molecule comes to rest at the surface of a solid its kinetic energy, or energy of motion, must be dissipated and is converted to heat. Thus an adsorption process is heat producing, or exothermic. Most large beds of adsorbing material require some means of cooling to carry off the heat.

After the molecules of a gas or vapor are adsorbed on a solid it is important for them to be held there, or retained, until it is convenient for them to be removed under controlled conditions so that the odor does not get in the atmosphere again. Retentivity plus the activity, or ability of the material to adsorb, are thus a total measure of the practical capacity of the adsorbing material. Activated carbon is good on both counts for many gases and vapors.

An adsorbing material has a limit in the number of molecules it can adsorb. When this point is reached, the carbon can be reactivated by passing steam through the adsorbing bed. The odorous material goes with the steam, from which it may be recovered by various processes, including fractional distillation.

IV. Equipment

1. Oilless gas pump (approximately 2 liters per minute capacity).
2. Pyrex U-tube, packed with Raschig rings or glass beads, or small flask, to hold odorous material.
3. Beaker to hold U-tube.
4. Two large diameter Pyrex tubes, 1½″ × 10″ long, to hold activated carbon. Flasks may be used if necessary.
5. Rotameter or other means of measuring rate of gas flow.

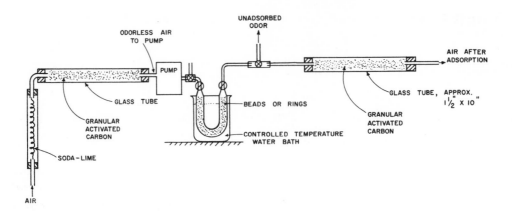

Figure 28-1 APPARATUS FOR ADSORPTION OF ODOR

6. Glass or plastic tubing.

7. Stopcocks or pinchcocks.

8. Rubber stoppers for U-tube and for tubes containing activated carbon and soda-lime.

9. Soda-lime tube.

V. Reagents and Materials

1. Odorous material to be selected by students, perhaps representing local conditions. (Food processing or kitchen wastes, commercial fertilizer, sewage treatment plant effluent, etc.)

2. Granular activated carbon.

3. Soda-lime.

VI. Procedure

1. Assemble the apparatus as illustrated in Fig. 28-1. If the odorous material is a liquid or gas, use the U-tube; if solid, use the small flask. (Soda-lime and activated carbon are used ahead of the pump to remove any acid aerosols or odors which might be present in the laboratory air and which could interfere with perception of odor reduction in the sample.)

2. Place the odorous material in its container. If liquid is used, the Raschig rings or beads should be thoroughly wetted by it.

3. Fill the glass tubes, or flasks, with the granular activated carbon and replace the stoppers. Fill the soda-lime tube similarly.

4. Start the gas pump and adjust the rate of air flowing through the system to that which will pass through the system without excessive pressure build-up. (In other words, rate of air flow measured by the rotameter at the system discharge

should not be appreciably less than that at the discharge of the pump itself.)

5. Turn the plug valve ahead of the adsorber tube to by-pass the adsorbing material and note the odor of the air being exhausted.

6. Turn the plug valve to pass the odorous air through the adsorber, and note the odor of the air being exhausted from the system.

7. If air exhausted from the adsorber is not odorless, open the bleeder valve at the pump discharge to reduce the load on the absorber until air leaving the adsorber is odorless. Measure the flow rate of air being discharged from the system.

VII. Records

Keep careful and neat records of the system used:

1. Volume and weight of adsorbing material used to reduce the odor being investigated.

2. Rate of air flow at which greatest reduction of odor is realized.

3. Kind of odorous material being investigated.

4. Your best estimate of the % by which odor was reduced.

VIII. References

1. A. C. Stern, Air Pollution (Vol. III); Academic Press, 2nd ed., 1968.

2. J. H. Perry, Chemical Engineer's Handbook; McGraw-Hill, 3rd ed., 1950.

3. Walker, Lewis, and McAdams, Principles of Chemical Engineering; McGraw-Hill, 1927.

IX. Prepared by Donald C. Hunter

EXPERIMENT NO. 29

Reduction of Odors by Direct-Flame Oxidation

I. Object

1. To demonstrate how objectionable odors can be destroyed by exposing the materials producing them to a flame under proper conditions.

2. To demonstrate that combustion gases have an odor different than that of air, but are of a low odor intensity and usually not objectionable.

II. Suitability and Usefulness

1. Can be used as a demonstration project.

2. The experiment can be expanded to various types of odor sources; however, caution should be exercised to limit the tests to those odorous compounds to which direct-flame oxidation is applicable.

III. Theory

Direct-flame oxidation is a type of high temperature oxidation in which organic odorous compounds can be destroyed by exposing them to a consuming flame in the presence of air. The odor producing compounds are oxidized to harmless gaseous products, such as carbon dioxide and water vapor.

Odors related to certain inorganic compounds such as hydrogen sulfide, ammonia, or cyanides can also be destroyed, depending on concentrations. There is a limit to the concentration of inorganic odorous compounds which can be treated in this manner because these contaminants are converted to oxides, such as sulfur oxides or nitrogen oxides, which are objectionable in themselves when present in significant concentrations.

Odors which ordinarily cannot be satisfactorily destroyed by high temperature oxidation alone, are those involved in waste gases containing halogen compounds or compounds, such as phosphates, which would form offensive oxides or acids. When waste gases containing halogen compounds are oxidized, the reaction products include free halogens or halogen acids, both of which are toxic and would have to be removed by chemical scrubbing before being discharged to the atmosphere. In the case of phosphates, the waste gases would contain phosphorous oxides or acids which are objectionable and would have to be removed by other means. (Chemical scrubbing and other means of treatment involving water may create a water pollution problem and must be carefully evaluated.)

In direct-flame oxidation, the odorous gases and vapors are destroyed at temperatures of 800 to 1500°F. The actual temperature required to do an effective job depends on the specific odorous contaminant and on the design of the burner and combustion chamber. (Ref. 1)

IV. Equipment

1. Gas pump $\frac{1}{10}$ HP—120 volts, Model 1531 —approximately 2 to 4 cubic feet of air per hour.

2. $\frac{1}{4}''$ needle valve or globe valve to adjust flow rate.

3. Rotameter to monitor flow. Brooks—0 to 6 SCFH (Standard cubic feet per hour).

4. Vaporizer—consisting of a U-Tube, 200 mm high (approx. 12 mm ID), equipped with 3 to 5-mm glass beads (No. 3000) and #2 Rubber Stoppers.

5. Combustion chamber—constructed of $1\frac{1}{2}''$ schedule 40 steel pipe 12'' long, wrapped with 2'' of Pressed Asbestos KAYCO insulation (or equivalent) equipped with a $\frac{1}{4}''$ OD copper or steel nipple mounted 2'' from the bottom.

6. Ring stand to mount combustion chamber.

7. Natural Gas Burner—Fisher $8\frac{1}{2}$ H with 40-mm diameter grid.

Note: Any type of burner is suitable, provided it is of a size producing a flame which fills the cross-section of the pipe chamber to result in good mixing and to minimize by-passing of the odorous gas.

8. Gas Washing Impinger—500-ml. to use to monitor odors, as required.

9. Temperature Measuring Device—0 to 2000°F. Alnor Pyrometer Type 1760, direct reading, equipped with 6' long 20-gauge chromel-alumel thermocouple.

10. Becton-Dickinson Syring with Luer-lok Tip, 100-ml capacity, to monitor odor.

11. Miscellaneous Teflon Tubing, $\frac{1}{4}''$ glass tees, and $\frac{5}{8}''$ capacity pinch clamps.

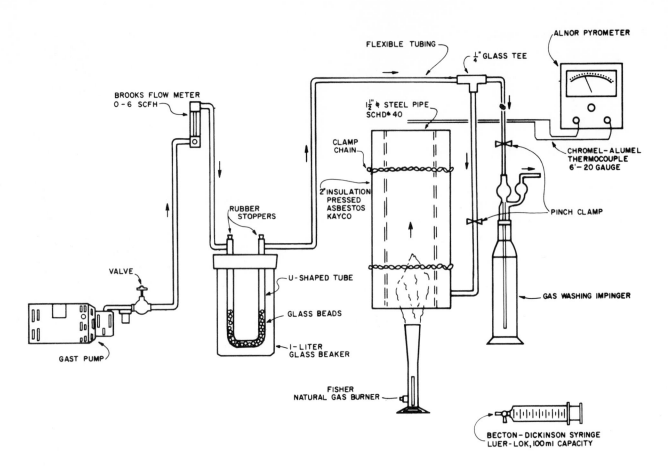

FIG. 29-1 ELIMINATION OF ODORS BY DIRECT FLAME OXIDATION

V. Reagents

Odorous materials for oxidation. Do not select compounds containing halogens or compounds, such as phosphates, which form offensive inorganic compounds. Ask our teacher to help in the selection. (In preparing this experiment, tests were conducted using alcohols and sulfides in low concentrations.)

VI. Procedure

Assemble the apparatus as shown in Figure 29-1 and in Figure 29-2.

1. Place 1 ml of odorous reagent in the U-tube together with 50 ml of water.

2. Fill the water bubbler with distilled water.

3. Light the gas burner and mount it in such a way that its top is at the bottom of the combustion chamber. Adjust the size of the flame so that it fills at least several inches of the combustion chamber length, but not to the extent that flames are carried to the top.

4. Start the air pump and adjust the flow rate to approximately 2 cu. ft. per hour. Open the pinch clamp, permitting the odorous air to go through the bubbler.

5. Using the 100-mm. syringe, sample the air exhausting from the bubbler. Reverse the syringe plunger, hold the discharge close to the nose, and observe the odor emitted. Observe and record the nature and relative intensity of the odor emitted for a given air flow rate. Odor intensity may be rated in 5 steps; 0—No odor, 1—Slight odor, 2—Definite odor, 3—Strong odor and 4—Overpowering odor.

6. Open the pinch clamp directing the odorous gas to the direct flame oxidizer. Close the pinch clamp directing the gas toward the bubbler. Adjust the air flow rate to the same rate used for the bubbler. Measure and record the temperature of the exhaust gases leaving the direct flame oxidizer. It should be between 800 and 1400°F.

7. Using the syringe, sample the gases at the top

of the combustion chamber. Again, observe and record the nature and relative intensity of the odor emitted.

8. By adjusting the size of the burner flame, determine the lowest temperature at which satisfactory odor destruction is achieved.

VII. Tests and Discussion

1. Note the characteristic odor of the burner gases without any odorous compounds introduced. Is it strong? Is it objectionable?

2. Determine the temperature required to satisfactorily oxidize various types of odorous compounds.

3. Compare the odors emitted from the bubbler with that of the direct-flame oxidizer at various temperatures.

Does the character of the odor change when the oxidizer is operated at different temperatures? How might the odor change with different flows through the oxidizer?

Note: At lower temperatures, or with a poorly designed combustion chamber, the gases exhausted may become more objectionable than the original gases, due to the formation of partially oxidized derivatives.

VIII. References

1. D. Benforado, Control of Solvent Emissions by Incineration; Metropolitan Engineers Council on Air Resources, 1967. (Library of Congress Cat. Card No. 67-31639.)

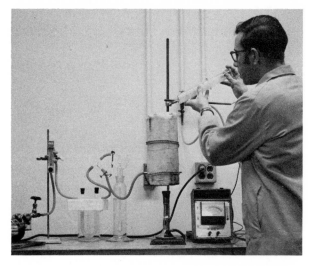

Fig. 29-2.   Sample being taken for odor determination.

2. John Mills, et al, Quantitative Odor Measurements; *Journal of Air Pollution Control Association,* **13,** 467–474, 1963.

3. D. M. Benforado, W. Rotella, and D. Horton, Development of an Odor Panel for Evaluation of Odor Control Equipment; *Journal of Air Pollution Control Association,* **19,** 101–105, 1969.

IX.   Prepared by David M. Benforado. Assistance by Michael Bolduc, H. J. Paulus, A. Dressler, D. A. Corliss, and R. F. McCurdy.

EXPERIMENT NO. 30

Use of the Electrostatic Precipitator in Removing Particles from Gases

I. Object

1. To demonstrate the removal of solid particles from a stack gas.

2. To illustrate the behavior of small particles in an electric field.

II. Suitability and Usefulness

1. Excellent for a demonstration project by senior high school physics students.

2. Teaches the behavior of small particles in an electric field of high voltage.

3. Teaches the principle of one method of cleaning air.

III. Theory

All combustion processes and many industrial and non-industrial operations produce small particles which are carried in suspension by the waste gases. This can also be true in some instances when the waste gas is only air. Examples of the latter might be flour milling or a rock crushing operation. The smoke from burning coal or a pile of burning leaves gets its darkness from the nature and density of the small particles resulting from the process. Black coal smoke gets its color from carbon particles due to incomplete combustion, possibly because not enough air is supplied

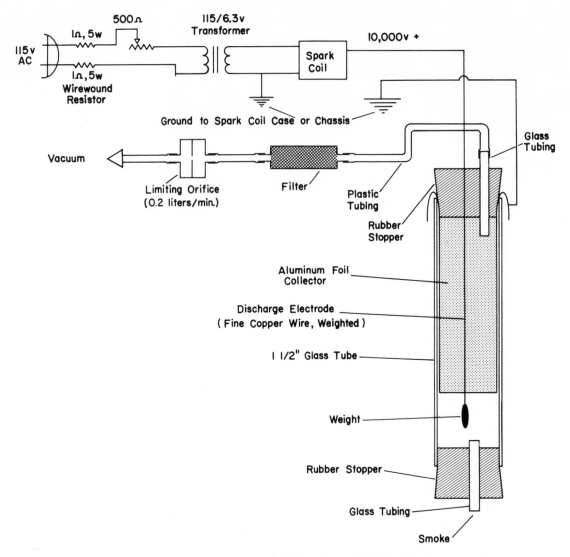

Fig. 30-1. ELECTROSTATIC PRECIPITATOR

for draft. The light gray smoke from a pile of burning leaves can result from small particles of both unburned leaves and ash. Much of the color in tobacco smoke is due to small particles, such as unburned tar, contained in it.

Most industrial processes have need for the removal of particles from waste gases, either to reduce air pollution or to recover valuable metals or other materials. To separate the particles from the gas stream, force must be applied. This force can be mechanical, such as centrifugal force used in the cyclone separator, or electrical, such as used in the electrostatic precipitator. In the latter, the separating force is based on Coulomb's law, which states that the force which acts to separate

the particle from the gas stream is proportional to the product of the electric charge on the particle and the intensity of the electric field to which the charged particle is attracted. Resisting separation are forces such as those due to velocity, turbulence, and viscosity of the gas stream.

It is from these basic principles that the electrostatic precipitator had its origin. The Greeks had known, probably as early as 600 B.C., that rubbed amber possessed an attraction for small particles and fibers. The electrostatic force involved was investigated by Coulomb during the 18th century. Attempts during the 19th century were made to build electrostatic precipitators, but it remained for Frederick G. Cottrell around

1905 to design the first successful electrostatic means of removing particles from waste gases. Modern precipitators may be small to huge in size and are capable of removing 95% to more than 99.9% of particles ranging from less than 0.10 μ up to more than 200 μ effective diameter. *Note:* Students should look up and memorize the definition of a micron (μ).

IV. Equipment

1. A 1½-inch diameter glass tube, approximately 8 inches long.

2. Fine copper wire, approximately 8 inches long, for the discharge electrode.

3. Aluminum foil.

4. Assembly consisting of a Ford spark coil, filament transformer (115 v to 6.3 v), and a spark gap. The assembly should be able to deliver 10,000 to 12,000 volts from a 115-volt AC power line. A rheostat in the primary of the transformer permits variation of spark voltage. The assembly should have an RF filter on the AC primary and high voltage RF suppression on the spark coil side. (As surplus equipment, the assembly can be purchased from Herbach and Rademan, Inc., 1204 Arch Street, Philadelphia, Pennsylvania 19107 for approximately $6.00.)

Note: If DC voltage is desired, a suitable rectifier can be purchased for about $20.00.

5. Source of vacuum, either aspirator or pump.

6. Limiting orifice, calibrated for maximum flow of approximately 0.2 liters/min. (May be obtained from Gelman Instrument Co., Box 1448, Ann Arbor, Michigan 48106.) A rotameter may also be used.

7. Small filter to prevent solid particles from plugging the limiting orifice.

8. Rubber stoppers for 1½-inch glass tube.

9. Plastic or rubber tubing, approximately 3/16-inch I.D.

10. Insulated copper wire with spring-clip connectors, to connect precipitator electrodes to spark coil and ground.

11. Glass tubing.

12. Small metal weight for discharge electrode wire.

V. Procedure

1. Assemble the equipment according to Fig. 30-1, mounting the 1½-inch glass tube in a clamp on a ring stand.

a. The stopper for the upper end should be bored on center to hold the discharge electrode wire snugly. A second hole at one side should be bored to hold a short length of glass tubing. The stopper for the lower end should be bored to hold a short length of glass tubing.

b. Pass the discharge electrode wire through the upper stopper so that it extends about 1 inch above the top.

c. Cut a rectangle of aluminum foil 8″ long × 2½″ wide. Place it in the tube so that it lines about one-half of the inside circumference and extends about 1 inch above the top of the 1½″ glass tube. Fold the top of the foil down against the outside of the tube.

d. Insert the upper and lower stoppers containing the wire and short pieces of glass tubing. The wire, when weighted, should then hang vertically and essentially on the center line of the 1½″ glass tube.

e. Connect the glass tubing in the upper stopper to the source of vacuum, being sure to insert the filter and the limiting orifice at convenient points. The filter can be made by placing glass wool or cigaret filters in a short length of plastic or glass tubing.

f. Connect the positive terminal of the spark coil to the foil and the negative terminal to the top of the discharge electrode wire.

2. Start the source of vacuum, drawing air at 0.2 liters/min. through the apparatus.

3. Connect the power-pack assembly to a 115-volt outlet. (*Caution*—Do not touch any of the electric terminals. The high voltage could give a severe shock.)

4. Attach an ammonium chloride smoke generator, a cigaret, or other source of smoke or dust particles to the tubing at the lower stopper. A small hole drilled in the smoke pipe of the school furnace might be used as a source of smoke.

5. Note that the particles become charged and migrate to the foil.

VI. References

1. Industrial Electrostatic Precipitation; Harry J. White; Addison-Wesley Publishing Company, Inc., 1963.

VII. Prepared by Donald C. Hunter Experimental work by: Thomas Moran

EXPERIMENT NO. 31

Design of a Kinetic Wet Air Cleaner

I. Object

1. To demonstrate one method of removing small particles from a stream of moving gas.
2. To illustrate the effects on a particle when the gas is accelerated to a higher velocity.

II. Suitability and Usefulness

1. Project demonstrates one principle used to remove particulate pollution from waste gases.
2. The project has a dramatic visual impact if the equipment is constructed of transparent plastic materials.
3. This project is suggested as a long term undertaking. The apparatus should be carefully designed, and meticulously constructed to insure the desired results. Therefore, it will require some time to plan and construct.

III. Theory

The control of atmospheric pollution, once a localized demand, is now an international necessity. Over the last few decades, man has poured billions of tons of destructive pollutants into the air causing damage to property, plants, animals, and himself.

Airborne wastes, whether they be gases, fumes, or solid particles, must not be allowed to pollute our atmosphere. For more than a hundred years, man has been searching for, discovering, testing, and adapting various types of equipment to remove such substances from industrial smoke stacks and working areas.

Pollution particles of sufficient size can be removed by using the principles of gravitational and centrifugal force. This does not, however, provide for the removal of smaller particles; therefore, another method of removing medium and small size particles was found.

One such method utilizes kinetic energy to bring about the impaction of a dust or fume particle on a water droplet of sufficient size to be removed from the air stream by gravity, centrifugal force, or some other appropriate method.

A small particle suspended in a stream of moving air attains the same velocity (kinetic energy) as the stream of air. Small water droplets injected into the moving stream of air have a lower velocity relative to the pollution particles. As the moving air molecules approach some target or object such as a water droplet, in their path, they must diverge to pass the object. The inertia of the pollution particle carried by the air stream tends to keep it on its original course, providing the possibility of collision with the target object. This is called impaction.

A particle with a higher velocity has a better chance of striking the target and sticking to it, and less chance of diverging around the target along with the air stream. Therefore, it is beneficial to accelerate the gas to a higher velocity. This is done by adding pressure energy to the air stream with a fan or compressor. This is then changed into kinetic energy (gas velocity) by forcing the stream of air through a funnel shaped duct called an acceleration section. The air stream attains its highest velocity at the throat of the apparatus where a sheet of water is injected perpendicular to the flow of the air stream. Here, impaction occurs and the water droplets collect the pollution particles.

IV. Equipment

1. Vacuum cleaner with connection for hose attachment.
2. Impeller type water pump (unless city water pressure is used).
3. Hose and connections capable of withstanding water pressure (30 to 40 lbs. per sq. in. if pump is used; 70 to 80 lbs. per sq. in. if city water pressure is used).
4. Specifically calibrated spray nozzles.
5. Water storage tank (suggest using plastic kitchen waste basket).

V. Reagents

Non-water-soluble pollutant (paint pigment, road dust, powdered iron oxide, any type of fume or smoke).

VI. Procedure

The first step in designing and building a kinetic wet air scrubber, is to find a source of pressure energy for the air stream. A standard home vacuum cleaner will prove to work quite well, and being quite common, should not require any financial expense. Make sure that the vacuum cleaner has provision for a hose to connect it to the remainder of the apparatus.

The entire project should be designed around the capacity of the vacuum cleaner; therefore, a fan performance curve should be secured for this machine. Most vacuum cleaner companies will be glad to supply this information. The curve should have the air flow volume in cubic feet per minute plotted along the horizontal axis, and the suction in inches water gauge plotted along the vertical axis (see Fig. 31-1).

The next step consists of determining the operating volume rate for the scrubber. The negative pressure at the vacuum cleaner should be 20 to 25 inches water gauge to insure that the impaction rate on the water droplets is great enough. To find the volume rate, first find the point on the graph where the negative pressure is in the desired range (20 to 25 inches), and then find the corresponding volume figure (cubic feet per minute).

The required velocity of the air stream at the point where the water is injected into the stream, is 12,000 to 24,000 feet per minute. Since the volume of air passing through a certain space per unit time is equal to the average velocity of the air times the area of the opening (Quantity = Area × Velocity), the size of the throat opening can easily be determined.

For example, if the air flow were 25 cubic feet per minute, and the required velocity were 17,500 feet per minute, the opening would have to be .001428 square foot, or .206 square inch (Area = 25 ft.^{3}/min./17,500 fg./min.).

After the gas has been speeded up to this velocity, a sheet of water is injected into the air flow. The water injection rate for this type of apparatus is usually 8 to 10 gallons per 1,000 cubic feet of air. Therefore, with our sample volume of 25 cubic feet per minute, the water injection rate would be 0.20 gallons per minute (8 gal./1,000 ft.^{3} × 25 ft.^{3}/ min. = 0.20 gal. per min.). This water should be very carefully injected into the air stream with either one or two spray nozzles (one nozzle would be sufficient for adequate throat coverage; however, a nozzle on each side would insure greater coverage). The nozzles can be secured from almost any farm spray equipment company. The nozzles may have to be specifically ordered because they will

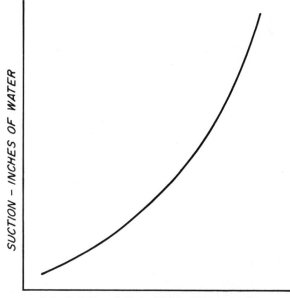

FIG. 31-1
TYPICAL FAN PERFORMANCE CURVE

have to handle the exact water volume at the desired water pressure.

The water should be forced through the nozzles at a fairly high pressure (at least 30 lbs. per square inch). Unless the project is to be self-contained, city water pressure may be used; however, this will require heavier hoses and connections. If the project is to be self-contained, a system for recirculating the water will have to be devised. The water pump will have to be selected to match the specifications of the spray nozzles.

After passing through the throat of the scrubber, the air and dirty water stream is decelerated to a velocity of about 4,000 feet per minute. It then enters a cylindrical section. Due to the position of the entering stream (tangent to the arc formed by the inside wall of the cylinder), the water droplets begin spinning around and around in the cylinder. As the centrifugal forces fling the water droplets to the walls of the cylinder where they drain to the bottom and out of the separator, the clean air continues to travel towards the top where it leaves through a smaller tube located within the larger cylinder. This tube receives the air through an

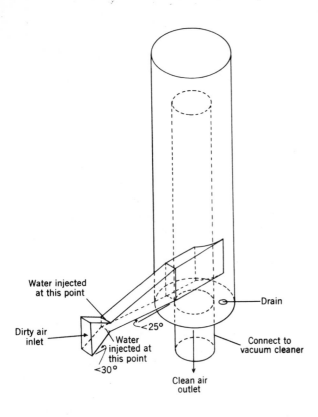

Water injected at this point

Dirty air inlet

Water injected at this point

<30°

<25°

Drain

Connect to vacuum cleaner

Clean air outlet

Fig. 31-2 Line drawing of assembled air cleaning apparatus

opening located near the top and exhausts it through the bottom of the cylinder (see Fig. 31-2).

Great care should be taken in designing the acceleration and deceleration sections. The primary angle of the acceleration section should not exceed 30 degrees from the horizontal, or there may be too much resistance to the air flow. Likewise, the deceleration section should not have a primary angle greater than 25 degrees, or great turbulence will be created as the fast moving gases expand (see Fig. 31-2).

Great care must also be taken to make sure that all connections and joints are air and water tight. The apparatus can be constructed out of metal but, for a more striking visual effect, clear plastic is more effective. Sheets of thin (⅛ inch) plastic, and clear plastic tubing for the separator section can be obtained at plastic supply houses.

In a practical application, this method could be used to recover valuable materials from the waste gas stream. The particles could be filtered from the water, and converted into useful products, or recycled. This method of air purification is superior to dry collection types because most dusts, once collected dry, are easily released back into the air and present a disposal problem. The collected particles from a wet kinetic type air scrubber can be disposed of easily, but they should not be dumped so they can wash into a stream and thereby create a water pollution problem.

VII. Observations

Efficiency of the apparatus in cleaning the air can be determined qualitatively by placing a sheet of filter paper between the clean air outlet and the vacuum cleaner and noting whether the filter remains clean. You may have to increase the voltage supplied to the vacuum cleaner motor so that air flow rate will remain at its pre-determined level.

You can also evaporate the water from the "dirty water" collected, weight the dried particles on an analytical balance, and relate weight of particles collected to total volume of air which passed through the apparatus. Results can be expressed in micrograms of particles per cubic meter of air.

VIII. Records

Keep complete and legible records of your design computations and of your observations.

IX. References

1. "WOW!!!" *Clean Air for New York State,* Vol. VII, No. 1 (Jan.–Feb., 1968).
2. The New York State Action for Clean Air Committee, New York State Department of Health, *Tips on How to Reduce Air Pollution, Fuel Oil Wastes, and High Heating Costs* (Published July, 1969).
3. "Air Pollution Damages Crops," *Clean Air for New York State,* Vol. VII, No. 1 (Jan.–Feb., 1968).
4. Albert B. Carr, *Teaching about Air Pollution* (Reprinted with permission from *School Science and Mathematics*); New York State Department of Health, Division of Air Resources, 84 Holland Avenue, Albany, New York 12208.
5. Lou Dickie, *All about Wet Collectors* (Reprinted courtesy of *Air Engineering*); American Air Filter Company, Inc., Louisville, Kentucky.

X. Prepared by James R. Griggs

(*Editor's Note:* This project won Mr. Griggs honors in the Westinghouse Science Talent Search, 1971. The report on the project was selected for inclusion by the Iowa Junior Academy of Science Symposium in Dubuque, Iowa, on April 23, and the NASA-NSTA Youth Science Congress in Minneapolis, Minn., on April 29–May 1. The project won four awards at the 1971 Hawkeye Science Fair in Des Moines, Iowa.)

EXPERIMENT NO. 32

Effect of Stack Height on Plume

I. Object

1. To demonstrate the effect of stack height on the plume; the higher the stack the higher the plume is displaced upward from ground-level with resulting lower gas concentrations at ground level.

II. Suitability and Usefulness

1. Causes the student to be aware of one of the particular air pollution control measures that may be taken by an industry to reduce pollutant concentrations at ground-level.

2. This experiment should be performed under the direct supervision of the teacher.

III. Theory and Background

Many heights of stacks are evident today to anyone who travels or lives near industrial or urban areas. Stack heights vary from short stubby chimneys on private homes to the very high stacks on factories, power plants and nuclear reactors. The stacks are usually constructed from steel, concrete, firebrick or a combination of these.

The primary function of a stack is to displace the smoke and gases high enough above the ground to prevent them from harming people, vegetation and property. A high stack vents these gases into winds which disperse them rapidly. There are several factors which help determine heights of stacks:

a. Size and operation of the plant

b. Height of buildings or obstacles near the plant

c. Nature of surrounding terrain—hills, mountains or valleys

d. Local weather conditions—especially the average wind speed and direction.

Usually, the larger the plant and its operation, the higher the stack. Studies have indicated that the stack should be at least $2\frac{1}{2}$ times taller than the nearest building or obstacle. This is to prevent turbulence, induced by these obstacles, from bringing the plume to the ground rapidly, and near to the stack. Plant managers want to be certain that the plume passes well above nearby hills where people live; they will also want to know the average wind speed and direction so they will be aware of where the plume travels after leaving the stack. Another factor enters too—the resulting ground-level concentrations of the gas at a distance from the stack. Equations are used to estimate these concentrations. As one travels away from the stack, the concentration first rises to a maximum then decreases to near zero. Two rules of thumb are:

a. Concentration of smoke at ground-level rises to a maximum at a distance proportional to the height of the stack and falls to zero with increasing distance downwind. A simple equation is:

$$X \max \alpha\, H$$

b. The maximum concentration at ground-level is directly proportional to the amount of gases issuing from the stack, and inversely proportional to the wind speed and the square of the stack height; $C \max \alpha\, Q/uH^2$

$X \max$ = distance of maximum concentration

$C \max$ = maximum concentration

H = stack height

u = wind speed

Q = amount of smoke and gases issuing from stack.

A simple graph looks like this:

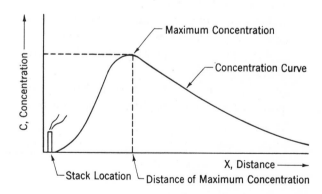

Stacks are limited in height due to economy and the expense involved in building them. Besides height, there are other methods by which ground level concentrations may be reduced. "Scrubbers" or "precipitators" are either used separately or in combination. Smoke and gases pass through these before entering the stack and are reduced. Stacks presently are built to 1000 feet; this is likely as high as they will get for some time.

IV. Equipment

1. A ventilation smoke tube. They may be ordered from: Mine Safety Appliances Company, 201 North Braddock Avenue, Pittsburgh, Pennsylvania 15208. Ask for #08-5645 smoke tube. A box of 12 tubes costs $8.00. (The company may send ·one for educational demonstration purposes without charge.)

2. One to two feet of flexible tubing—rubber, etc.

3. A small electric fan.

4. A small vacuum pump normally used in a laboratory. The exhaust should be fitted with a control valve to gauge the velocity of exhaust. (Some pumps may have these valves.)

5. A ringstand with test-tube holder affixed to vertical post.

V. Procedure

1. Attach tubing to exhaust control outlet on pump.

2. Attach smoke tube in vertical position using test-tube clamp on stand. Fasten to near the top of stand post and measure the height of the top of the tube above the table surface. Record height.

3. Snip off lower end of smoke tube and attach tubing.

4. Snip off top end of smoke tube. (Recheck height of tube top.)

5. Place fan 3 to 5 feet from tube and direct fan at tube. Turn on. Direct flow to near top of tube.

6. Turn on vacuum pump, setting the control valve to *low* velocity.

7. Note plume height and characteristic, and downwind in stack's lee. Measure distance from the stack to where plume *first* strikes table surface. (To curtail or stop smoke, turn off pump; limit the *smoke* amount; it *has a pungent odor, causing eye, nose and throat irritation.*) Record Distance.

8. Slide test tube clamp with tube to *lower* position on vertical post. Remeasure (1) height of stack and (2) distance where plume *first* strikes table surface. Record stack height and distance.

9. If fan is turned off, the smoke will indicate air currents in classroom or laboratory; it will tend to rise toward ceiling if air conditioning is operating. The fan will give plume direction which is more realistic to out-of-doors conditions.

10. If a vacuum pump is unavailable, a hand-squeeze bulb may be substituted. The end opposite to that which the rubber tubing is attached should have a one-way flow valve to prevent smoke from issuing from bottom of bulb.

11. A hood in a laboratory may be used at the instructor's option. (If hood is used, be sure ventilation draft does not affect plume.)

Note to Teacher: If desired, the ammonium chloride smoke generator (see Experiment No. 25) may be used instead of the ventilation smoke tube.

VI. Discussion Question

1. Can a relationship be found between the stack height and the distance where the plume first strikes the table surface?

VIII. References

1. Pasquill, F., *Atmospheric Diffusion,* D. Van Nostrand Ltd., New York, 1962.

2. Stern, Arthur C., *Air Pollution: Volume One,* 2nd edition, Academic Press, New York, 1968.

3. Sutton, O. G., *Micrometeorology,* McGraw-Hill Book Company, New York, 1953.

VIII. Prepared by Victor H. Sussman

EXPERIMENT NO. 33

Effect of Stack Gas Velocity on Height of the Plume

I. Object

1. To demonstrate the effect of stack gas velocity on plume height; a high velocity will buoy the plume higher into the air than a low gas velocity.
2. To demonstrate the effect of wind speed upon the height of the plume.

II. Suitability and Usefulness

1. A stack gas velocity increase is one air pollution control measure plants may take to reduce nearby ground-level smoke and gas concentrations.
2. To make the observer aware that increase in wind speeds significantly reduce plume height.
3. This experiment should be performed under the direct supervision of the teacher.

III. Theory and Background

Stacks are used to displace and disperse smoke and gases into higher levels of the atmosphere to maintain low ground level gas and smoke concentrations. These low concentrations are necessary to eliminate or minimize adverse ground-level concentrations which may be harmful to people, vegetation and property. Stack heights may be designed or estimated by using these criteria:

    a. Size and operation of the plant;

    b. Height of buildings or obstacles near the plant;

    c. Nature of surrounding terrain—hills, mountains, valleys; and

    d. Local weather conditions especially the average wind speed and direction.

The stack should be at least $2\frac{1}{2}$ times taller than the nearest obstacles to prevent downwash of the plume. Downwash is caused by wind eddies induced by obstacles which bring the plume rapidly to ground-level.

To cause the plume to travel to greater altitudes, plants induce forced drafts into the stack, which increase the stack gas velocity. Usually the stack gas velocity is defined as that velocity present at the *top* of the stack. This is called the stack gas *exit* velocity. Besides induced drafts, an increase in heat output or rate of combustion will increase stack gas exit velocity.

Principally the height of the plume above the stack is a function of four variables: (1) stack gas exit velocity; (2) temperature of the stack gas; (3) bouyancy of the plume as a result of the difference of the temperature of the plume itself and the surrounding air; and (4) wind speed. The height of plume above the *stack* is specifically called plume rise; however, the height of the plume above the *ground* is called the effective stack height. The effective *stack height* is defined as the combined heights of the physical stack itself and the plume rise. The level where the plume travels horizontally is usually the effective stack height.

An infinite increase of stack gas exit velocity will not bring about the desired results of a greatly extended effective stack height. If the stack gas exit velocity is increased too much by forced draft, the draft will cool and partially disorganize the plume causing it to decrease in effective stack height. An optimum exit velocity must be found and maintained for maximum effective height.

When the plume leaves the stack, it immediately comes under the influence of wind. As wind speeds increase, the plume is bent over progressively due to (1) the force of the wind; and (2) the cooling of the plume by rapid mixing with the surrounding air. During calm conditions the plume will rise vertically until it reaches a level where its momentum and buoyancy approach zero. This level is often defined by a warm layer or inversion in the atmosphere. Several investigators developed empirical formulas to estimate effective stack heights. Variables in these equations are: (1) the inside diameter of the stack at its top; (2) wind speed; (3) stack gas exit velocity; (4) stack gas temperature; (5) temperature of outside air; and (6) the difference between the stack gas and outside air temperatures. The last three variables may be used to compute heat output in terms of calories per second and by using the specific heat of the stack gas. Two equations shall be briefly reviewed.

The Davidson-Bryant plume rise equation is:

$$\Delta H = D \left(\frac{V_s}{u}\right)^{1.4} \left(1 + \frac{T_s - T_a}{T_s}\right)$$

where ΔH = plume rise above the stack, m

V_s = stack gas exit velocity, m sec^{-1}

u = average wind speed at stack level, m sec^{-1}

D = internal stack diameter at top, m

T_s = average absolute temperature of gases emitted from stack, °K

T_a = temperature of the ambient atmosphere, °K

Another equation is Holland's (simplified) formula:

$$\Delta H = \frac{V_s D}{n}\left(1.5 + 2.68 \frac{T_s - T_a}{T_s} D\right)$$

where all symbols and associated units are the same as the Davidson-Bryant formula. Plants design their stacks to try to take full advantage of plume rise conditions. They may select other formulas besides those listed here. A plume rise equation will not apply to a cool dense plume, which, after emerging from the stack, falls rapidly to ground-level.

IV. Equipment

1. A ventilation smoke tube. They may be ordered from: Mine Safety Appliances Company, 201 North Braddock Avenue, Pittsburgh, Pennsylvania 15208. Ask for #08-5645 ventilation smoke tube. A box of 12 tubes costs $8.00. (The company may send one for educational demonstration purposes without charge.)

2. One to two feet of flexible tubing.

3. A small electric fan.

4. A small vacuum pump normally used in a laboratory. The exhaust should be fitted with a control valve to gauge the velocity of exhaust. (Some pumps may have these valves.)

5. A stand with a test tube holder affixed to the vertical post.

V. Procedure

1. Attach tubing to exhaust valve outlet on pump.

2. Attach ventilation smoke tube, in vertical position, using test tube clamp on stand.

3. Snip off lower end of smoke tube with scissors and attach tubing.

4. Snip off top end of smoke tube. Measure tube top height.

5. Place fan about 5 to 7 feet from tube, directed at the apparatus.

6. Turn on vacuum pump—using *low* velocity. Note exist velocity and plume height (where plume begins to level off). Record height.

7. Increase velocity at pump and note plume characteristics. Measure plume height and record. Turn off pump (Note: keep smoke to minimum; *the smoke causes eye, nose and throat irritations*).

8. Turn on electric fan

9. Start vacuum pump—at low velocity. Note the "bent-over" plume. Measure and record (1) plume height; and (2) where plume first strikes table top.

10. Increase vacuum pump velocity and re-measure plume height and the distance from the stack where the plume first strikes table surface. Compare with Step 9 results. Note how an increase in stack gas velocity will decrease or eliminate downwash in lee of stack.

11. Any of the previous steps may be repeated to achieve desired results; intermediate plume heights and distances may be studied. When complete, turn off all equipment.

12. If the vacuum pump is unavailable, a hand-squeeze bulb may be used. The end opposite to that to which the tubing is attached should have a one-way flow valve to prevent smoke from issuing from the bottom of the bulb.

13. A hood in the laboratory may be used at the instructor's option.

Note to Teacher: If desired, the ammonium chloride generator (see Experiment No. 25) may be used instead of the ventilation smoke tube.

VI. Discussion Questions

1. Which is better: a tall stack or a high stack gas exit velocity?

2. How accurate did you find the equations for plume rise?

VII. References

1. Pasquill, F., *Atmospheric Diffusion*, D. Van Nostrand Ltd., New York, 1962.

2. Stern, Arthur C., *Air Pollution: Volume One*, 2nd edition Academic Press, New York, 1968.

3. Sutton, O. G., *Micrometeorology*, McGraw-Hill Book Company, New York, 1953.

VIII. Prepared by Victor H. Sussman

EXPERIMENT NO. 34

Use of Power Plant Fly Ash in Brick Manufacture

I. Object

1. To illustrate an interesting use for fly ash recovered by air cleaning devices in coal-burning electric power plants.

II. Suitability and Usefulness

1. Good as a demonstration project.
2. Teaches that an air pollution abatement practice can sometimes create useful materials instead of a solid waste disposal problem.
3. Exposes students to possible new frontiers of private enterprise.

III. Theory and Background

Traditionally brick has been made from clay, and brick yards have been located near a combination of the raw material and economical means of transportation for delivery to point of use. The largest markets for brick have been at or near large centers of population and often distant from point of manufacture, thus adding more in transportation to the cost of brick at the point of use.

It has been known for several years that power plant fly ash, or pulverized coal ash, has some properties similar to those of clay and considerable work has been done in substituting fly ash for part of the clay. More recently, it has been found that even better brick can be made from a combination of fly ash and bottom ash or boiler slag, bonded together with liquid sodium silicate. Bottom ash and boiler slag particles are coarser than fly ash and, because of their larger relative size, help release moisture during the drying operation. A typical formula is roughly 74% fly ash, 23% bottom ash or slag, and 3% sodium silicate (dry basis). Brick properties have been improved somewhat by modifying the mix formula as follows: 76.2% fly ash, 21.2% bottom ash or slag, and 2.6% sodium silicate (dry basis), with 9.9% water. (The dry constituents total 100%; the water is additional.) Part of the water is available in the liquid sodium silicate solution; the balance is added. The Coal Research Bureau of the School of Mines at West Virginia University has developed the process and has an experimental plant in operation at Morgantown, W. Va.

This brick has all of the performance qualities of clay brick, is about 30% lighter in weight, and usually costs considerably less to manufacture. Another advantage is that the raw materials, fly ash and bottom ash, are often close to centers of population or to the point of greatest use, thus making transportation cost a more favorable item.

The cleaning of stack gases in coal burning power plants to reduce air pollution has developed into a major solid waste disposal problem. Annual production of fly ash in the United States is expected to increase from 30 million tons in 1970 to 45 million tons in 1980 as more power is needed for the requirements of our population and industry. Up to now, use has been found for less than 10% of the fly ash produced, mostly in replacing part of the portland cement in concrete. Disposal of the remainder is costing power producers $2.00 per ton or more and is burying considerable land area. It is conceivable that this disposal problem, if allowed to grow, might force the abandonment of coal as a fuel for electric power production. Use of this material for brick can help alleviate the disposal problem and conserve our supplies of clay for future generations. The cost advantage may make brick preferable to wood for exterior and interior work, and thereby help conserve lumber as well.

IV. Equipment

1. Form for molding brick in 1-inch cube size (Fig. 34-1).
2. Lever operated press to apply 1,000 lbs./sq. in. pressure to the brick mixture in the mold. A simple press is illustrated in Fig. 34-1, in which the fulcrum is at the plunger applying pressure to the contents of the mold. If we desire to have a force of 1,000 lbs. acting downward at the mold, we must first consider well the directions of all forces involved and the directions of their equal and opposite reactions. With the right end of the lever chained to the floor and with a weight W applied at the left end and assuming the lever itself weightless, we have the situation illustrated in Fig. 34-1. The force W will be downward. The force P relative to the floor will be upward as the weight W

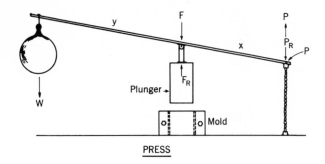

PRESS

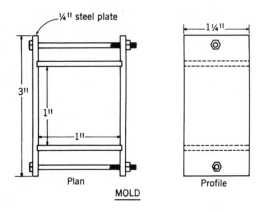

Plan   Profile

MOLD

Fig. 34-1 Lever and mold for brick specimen

is applied, but its reaction will be downward with respect to the plunger at the fulcrum. Although the force F being applied to the mold is downward, there is an equal and opposite reaction applied to the lever by the plunger. In other words, the plunger will try to bend the lever at the fulcrum as the lever bears down on it.

If we apply a weight W of 100 lbs. at the left end to get an upward force reaction of 1,000 lbs. at the fulcrum, the downward reaction to force P must be the difference, or 900 lbs., because at equilibrium opposing forces must be equal. But to achieve 1,000 lbs. at the fulcrum, W and P_R must be at the proper distances from the fulcrum. The weight W times its distance from the fulcrum must equal the downward reaction P_R times its distance from the fulcrum. (The steelyard was at one time a commonly used example of the principle, especially for weighing meat carcasses and other food products.) If we assume the distance x = 1 (one inch, one foot, etc.), then P = Wy; or y = 900/100 = 9. Thus for a weight of 100 lbs. and a weightless lever, x and y should be in the ratio of 1:9.

But a weightless lever would be without strength. Let's assume that the material selected weighs 10 lbs. per foot of length and that we shall keep a 10-ft total length with x and y remaining in the ratio of 1:9. The lever will have a weight of 100 lbs. For a system in equilibrium, the various forces times their distances from any selected point must have an algebraic sum of zero. If we consider our point at *P*,

$$(5 \times 100) + 10W - (1 \times 1000) = 0, \text{ or}$$
$$(5 \times 100) + 10W = (1 \times 1000)$$
$$10W = 1000 - 500 = 500$$
$$W = 50 \text{ lbs.}$$

Similarly, we can prove that there will be a 1,000-lb. force at the fulcrum:

$$(50 \times 10) + (100 \times 5) - (F_R \times 1) = 0$$
$$F_R = 1,000 \text{ lbs.}$$

Now if we add the forces algebraically, we find that P_R changes to

$$(50 + 90) + 10 + P_R = 1,000$$
$$P_R = 1000 - 150 = 850 \text{ lbs. downward.}$$

The tendency toward bending the lever at each side of the fulcrum will be 855 ft.-lbs. Consider your point at the fulcrum and prove it. (Remember that a continuous load, such as your lever, exerts a downward force equal to its weight at the middle of its length, according to the point around which bending stresses are being considered.)

Note: Other devices, such as hydraulic jacks or more complicated lever systems, might be considered, but safety of students should have first priority.

The plunger should make a snug fit with the inside of the mold to avoid having the mold contents forced out.

3. A suitable box or pail in which to mix the ingredients.

4. Drying oven capable of 210° to 220°F temperature.

5. Furnace to fire brick, preferably equipped with a forced air inlet. (Furnace used in the school's Art Department for firing pottery should be suitable.)

6. Set of Tyler sieve screens for grading bottom ash or slag.

V. Materials

1. Fly ash, from a nearby coal-burning power plant.

2. Bottom ash or slag, from the same nearby coal-burning plant; screen for uniform size; discard oversize and undersize fractions; particles retained

on a 30-mesh screen and passing a 10 or 14-mesh screen are preferred. (Sand may be used if bottom ash or slag is not available.)

3. Liquid sodium silicate (water glass) having a specific gravity of 47° on the Baumé scale, obtainable from any chemical supply house.

4. Pyrometric cones to indicate firing furnace temperature; when heated slowly, those deforming between 2000° and 2100° are #02, #01, #1, #2, and #3. Plaques to hold cones erect in oven. Both are obtainable from Edward Orton, Jr. Ceramic Foundation, Columbus, Ohio.

VI. Procedure

1. Dry mix sufficient fly ash and screened bottom ash or slag in the ratio of 76.2 parts by weight fly ash to 21.2 parts by weight of screened bottom ash or slag. (Students in some localities may find it advisable to alter this mix formula slightly because of differing ash properties due to the particular composition of the coal being burned.)

2. Add 6.0 parts by weight of liquid sodium silicate and 6.5 parts by weight of water to the dry mixture, and mix thoroughly in a figure 8 pattern. (This will amount to 2.6 percent sodium silicate on a dry basis and 9.9 parts by weight of water because the sodium silicate solution contains 43.1 percent dry silicate and 56.9 percent water. Note that the dry ingredients total 100% and that water is over and above.)

3. Transfer the mixture to the mold and apply 1000 lbs. per sq. in. pressure to the mixture for 30 seconds by means of the press described in IV. (In actual practice a molding pressure of 3,000 lbs. per sq. in. is used for regular size brick, but would be difficult to attain in a high school laboratory.)

4. Open the mold, remove the formed brick carefully, and set it aside to dry in warm air (an oven at 210°F to 220°F is preferable).

5. Place the dried brick and a pyrometric cone (which will deform and blend over at the desired temperature) in the forced air firing furnace, raise the temperature to 1,000°F, and hold it there for 2 to 3 hours to burn off any carbonaceous material. (*Note:* Special plaques are available to hold the cone in an upright position.) (Fly ash containing appreciably more carbon than usual will require a longer burn-off time.) Then increase the temperature at a rate of about 150°F per hour to a level of 2,000° to 2,100°F and hold that temperature until the selected pyrometric test cone softens and bends completely over. (Be careful not to raise the fur-

nace temperature so high that the test cone melts.) *Note:* In actual practice, three test cones are usually placed in the furnace—one to deform below the desired temperature, one at the desired temperature. This is done to warn the operator that the desired temperature is approaching and to indicate that it has not been exceeded.

6. Turn off the furnace. After it has cooled sufficiently, remove the brick and set it aside. Determine its exact dimensions.

7. If possible, take the fired brick to a nearby engineering school and ask the professor in charge to have it tested for compressive strength.

Note A: Students wishing to study gradation of color shade attainable in brick, may make several balls of the mixture by hand, dry them, put them in the firing furnace, burn off the carbon as above, and then remove them one by one as the firing temperature increases. Color shade should deepen with increase in temperature and amount of oxidation.

Note B: Inorganic pigment compounds might be added to the standard mixture for other color possibilities. Manganese dioxide will provide a chocolate to black color; titanium dioxide will produce a deep red.

Note C: Other students might wish to experiment with a mixture of fly ash, sawdust, and sodium silicate solution at different pressures to determine whether it is possible to produce a lightweight wallboard or building block, having good thermal and sound insulation properties. A French patent (No. 1,317,928, Feb. 1963) describes this and suggests a firing temperature of about 1.900°F for 2-½ hours after drying. A British patent (No. 1,121,572, July 1968) describes a similar product, using portland cement instead of sodium silicate and thus eliminating the need for firing. Students doing this should try different ingredient proportions until best product results are obtained. (Disposal of sawdust is often by an incinerator with low combustion efficiency, thus adding to air pollution problems. Uses for more of this waste material are needed.)

Note D: Is it possible to produce a glazed wall tile from fly ash? Who wants to try it?

VII. Keep complete and neat records of the following for each product you produce:

1. Source of fly ash and bottom ash or slag.

2. Average composition of coal burned, if available.

3. Source of coal burned in the power plant.

4. Weights of fly ash, bottom ash, sodium silicate solution, and additional water in your mix.

5. Pounds of pressure applied per square inch.

6. Duration of pressure application.

7. Duration of drying period.

8. Drying temperature.

9. Duration of firing.

10. Firing temperature.

11. Compressive strength in lbs./sq. in.

12. Dimensions of final product.

13. Color of product achieved as indicated by a color photograph.

VIII. Problems

1. A press of what capacity (in tons) would be needed to mold 12 full size bricks at a time in an actual brick plant, assuming pressure is applied to the largest surface area of each brick?

2. After completing the experiment, prepare a sketch illustrating the kind and size of equipment you think would be needed for a completely mechanized plant producing 5,000 bricks per 8-hour day. How much operating and maintenance labor do you think would be needed for efficient operation?

3. How could you re-design the lever system to produce a molding pressure of 1,000 lbs. per sq. in.,

using a weight of only 10 lbs. and without lengthening the lever?

IX. References

1. H. E. Shafer, Jr., C. F. Cockrell, K. K. Humphreys, J. W. Leonard, Status Report on Bricks from Fly Ash; U.S. Bureau of Mines Information Circular No. 8348, Fly Ash Utilization, Proceedings: Edison Electric Institute National Coal Association—Bureau of Mines Symposium, Pittsburgh, Pa., March 1967.

2. Author's discussions with Mr. Leonard and Mr. Humphreys and visit to the brick plant at West Virginia University, Sept. 1970.

X. Acknowledgment

The author is indebted to Mr. Leonard and Mr. Humphreys for their hospitality and for their kindness in reviewing the draft of this experiment and in suggesting changes for better clarity.

XI. Prepared by Donald C. Hunter

EXPERIMENT NO. 35

Use of Power Plant Fly Ash in Treating Polluted Waters

I. Object

1. To illustrate a useful role for a product of an air pollution abatement process.

II. Suitability and Usefulness

1. Good as a science demonstration.

2. Teaches students to look for unexpected uses for materials usually considered waste.

3. Brings home the point that an air pollution abatement process should not necessarily create another waste disposal problem.

4. Teaches something of water and waste water treatment.

5. Teaches students that use of waste products can conserve natural resources.

III. Theory and Background

Most coal-burning power plants utilize the rapid combustion of pulverized bituminous coal to produce heat to make high pressure steam which turns the turbine driving an alternating current generator. After the volatile matter and most of the carbon are burned, the incombustible portion, or ash, remains as solid particles, mostly spherical, ranging in diameter from 0.5 to 100 microns and with widely varying chemical and physical properties, depending on the fuel and operating conditions.

Power plant fly ash (perhaps better called "pulverized coal ash") consists principally of silica and alumina. The constituents may vary somewhat as follows in % by weight: silica (SiO_2) 20 to 60, alumina (Al_2O_3) 10 to 35, iron oxide (Fe_2O_3 or Fe_3O_4) 2 to 35, calcium oxide (CaO) 1 to 20, magnesium oxide (MgO) 0.3 to 4, titanium oxide (TiO_2) 0.5 to 2.5, alkalies (Na_2O and K_2O) 1 to 4, sulfur trioxide (SO_3) 0.1 to 4, and carbon (determined by loss on ignition) 0.4 to 36. While calcium is expressed as the oxide and sulfur as the trioxide, they may actually be combined as gypsum

(CaSO$_4$). The ash particles are usually various shades of gray, depending on the amount of carbon remaining in them. The amount of carbon remaining depends on efficiency of combustion—the more efficient the combustion the less carbon there will be.

Unless captured and removed from the combustion gases, the fly ash is carried with the gases up the stack and out into the atmosphere to pollute the air and settle over the surrounding countryside. Combustion also produces air polluting gases and vapors, some of which are considered in other experiments. To reduce the amount of air pollution, as much as possible of the fly ash is usually removed by electrostatic precipitators, cyclones, bag filters, or combinations of them.

It has been estimated that a one million-kilowatt power plant will produce about 1,000 tons of fly ash each day, that about 30 million tons were produced in the United States in 1970, and that in 1980 annual production will be 45 million tons as more and more power is generated to meet the demands of our ever-increasing population. Somewhat less than 10% of the fly ash now produced in the United States is used; the remainder is a solid waste disposal problem, costing up to $2 per ton to haul to available dump sites.

It has been reported that some fly ashes have properties making them well suited for use in treating various polluted waters. The most significant are adsorptive capacity, ability to release certain beneficial constituents to the water, and ability to settle readily in the water.

Adsorption

Because fly ash has relatively large surface area per unit volume and some residual carbon content, the ash may be used to remove many organic materials such as the sulfonates in detergents, phenols, and certain other organic materials such as color, taste, odor, bacteria, and algae. Degree of adsorption is proportional to carbon content of the ash.

Water Conditioning

Certain small quantities of materials in the ash, such as gypsum (CaSO$_4$), lime (CaO), and certain hydroxides, are soluble in water and produce their beneficial effects when water is treated with fly ash. Hydroxyl ions tend to increase the pH or make the water more alkaline, and should be effective in treating acid mine drainage. The calcium ions from the gypsum and lime have been found to remove phosphorus as a complex calcium phosphorus

hydroxyl ion when the water has reached sufficient alkalinity.

Settling

Because of its generally high specific gravity (approaching that of sand), the major portion of fly ash settles readily in a quiescent column of water. According to Stokes' Law, the particles are calculated to settle at a rate of about 0.5 foot per hour. Under actual conditions the ash has been found to settle considerably faster. This indicates that the particles may be agglomerating and settling as larger masses, thus carrying down their load of pollutants at the faster rate.

A small fraction of the particles have been reported not to settle, but to remain floating on the surface. These are small hollow glass-like spheres filled with nitrogen and are called cenospheres. Can you think of practical uses for them?

Note: Because fly ash from different sources varies widely in composition some students performing this experiment may obtain negative rather than positive results. This is not an uncommon experience of adults in performing their daily tasks. Negative results should not be interpreted as failure, but should whet the determination to perhaps try a new tack. That's how Thomas Edison invented the electric light bulb.

IV. Equipment

1. One-gallon glass jugs—two required.
2. 2-liter graduated cylinders—two required.
3. Pair of matched nessler tubes, 50 ml. tall form; with set of calibrated glass disc color standards. (If not available, test tubes can be substituted for a less quantitative determination.)
4. Total phosphate analyzer. (Kits are available for colorimetric determination at about $20 for phosphates alone up to $225 for an instrument capable of 30 some different water determinations. Two manufacturers are Hach Chemical Company, Box 907, Ames, Iowa 50010, and Delta Scientific, 120 E. Hoffman Ave., Lindenhurst, N.Y. 11757.)

V. Reagents and Materials

1. About 50 lbs of fresh, dry fly ash from a nearby coal-burning power plant. (Do not use fly ash that may have been lagooned because water will have leached away some of its important constituents.)

VI. Procedure

In view of the beneficial properties which research has shown power plant fly ash to have in treating polluted water, this experiment can consist of several parts as follows, some of which have been left for the student and teacher to formalize:

1. Reduction of turbidity and color.
2. Reduction of odor.
3. Reduction of bacteria count.
4. Reduction of algae growths.
5. Reduction of phosphorus content.
6. Neutralization of acid mine waste waters.

Using clean glass jugs (washed and rinsed with distilled water), collect water from a nearby river or lake. Use water from one jug for experimentation with fly ash as directed and from the other without fly ash as a control.

Turbidity

Turbidity in water is caused by the presence of suspended matter, such as clay, silt, finely divided organic matter, plankton, and other microscopic organisms. It is an expression of the optical property which causes light to be scattered and absorbed rather than transmitted in straight lines through the water sample. The standard method for determination of turbidity is the Jackson candle method, but other less accurate methods may be used if necessary for an estimation of the degree of turbidity. It is preferable to determine turbidity on the same day the sample is collected.

If the Jackson candle should be available, details of the method will be found in Reference No. 2. In using other instruments, the instructions of the manufacturer should be followed.

1. Fill each of the 2-liter graduated cylinders with water collected for examination and treatment.
2. Slowly add 2 grams of the dry power plant fly ash per liter of water to one of the cylinders.
3. After the fly ash has settled, compare the turbidity of the treated sample with that of the untreated sample. Do this with a turbidimeter if available. Otherwise, estimate the degree of turbidity remaining by comparison with your own standard.
4. If some turbidity remains in the treated sample, repeat steps 2 and 3 five times, using 4, 5, 10, 15, and 20 grams of fly ash per liter.
5. Prepare a graph, plotting turbidity vs. fly ash concentration.

Color

Color in water may result from the presence of natural metallic ions (such as iron and manganese), humus and peat materials, plankton and algae, weeds and various industrial wastes. The term "true color" water refers to that color remaining after all turbidity has been removed. Turbidity should be removed only by centrifuging the sample. Filtration is not acceptable because it may remove some of the true color as well as the turbidity. The color determination should be made soon after collecting the water sample because biologic changes occurring in storage may affect the color.

Note: If the sample water has insufficient color for a good demonstration of the effect of fly ash, color can be added by allowing the sample to leach color from mulched leaves and weeds under laboratory conditions.

1. Fill one of a matched pair of nessler tubes to the 50-ml. mark with the water to be examined.
2. Fill the other with the same volume of colorless distilled water.
3. Stand the two tubes on a white surface and note the difference in color as you look down through the water at the white surface. (If color comparison discs are available, place them one at a time between the tubes and the white surface. Match the color of the test water with the disc nearest in color.)
4. Using the test water, from which turbidity has been removed by centrifuging, fill one of the 2-liter cylinders and add 3 grams of fly ash per liter of water. Stir with a paddle at about 30 rpm for 15 minutes. Allow the fly ash to settle. Fill one of the matched pair of nessler tubes with the supernatant liquid and compare its color with that of the colorless distilled water as above.
5. Repeat step 4 five times, using 5, 10, 15, 20 and 30 grams per liter.
6. Plot color units vs. fly ash concentration on 10 × 10 graph paper.

Odor

Many polluted waters will be found to have some type of disagreeable odor. Detection and assessment of odor is a subjective determination. Some persons are more sensitive to odors than others. A good observer should have a sincere interest in conducting the test. Smoking and eating just before making the test, as well as the use of soaps, shaving lotions, and perfumes, should be avoided. Nor should the observer be suffering from a cold or the "sniffles." Do not add contamination by touching the neck of the flask containing the sample. The laboratory should likewise be as free as possible from odor.

It is best to smell several dilutions of the water

in question, starting with the most dilute and working progressively toward more concentrated solutions until odor is first detected. This is known as the threshold odor.

1. Add 200 ml., 50 ml., 12 ml., and 2.8 ml., of the odor-bearing water from one of the jugs to separate 500-ml. odor free glass-stoppered erlenmeyer flasks and dilute each to a total volume of 200 ml. by adding odor-free water. Add 200 ml. of odor-free water to another flask, which will serve as the reference.

Note: With certain badly polluted waters, 2.8 ml. of sample diluted to 200 ml. may be too concentrated to be below the threshold odor. If so, prepare other flasks with 2.0, 1.4, and 1.0 ml of sample diluted to 200 ml. with odor-free water.

2. Heat the water in each flask to 60°C and maintain it at that temperature.

3. Shake the flask containing the odor-free water, remove the stopper, and sniff the vapors.

4. Do likewise with the sample of lowest concentration. Compare it with the odor-free flask. If no odor can be detected in the sample, proceed to compare the odor-free flask with progressively more concentrated samples until an odor can be detected. Consider this the threshold and record the concentration.

5. If odor can be detected in the most dilute sample, prepare more dilute sample mixtures as noted above, and repeat the examination until a threshold is found.

6. Fill a 2-liter graduated cylinder with the sample water, add 20 grams of power plant fly ash, and stir very slowly for 15 minutes.

7. Allow fly ash to settle to the bottom.

8. Decant the clear liquid and repeat steps 1 through 5.

9. Note whether water treated with fly ash has a lower threshold odor than untreated water.

Question: Why have all odor test comparisons started with the most dilute concentration?

Phosphorus

This chemical element has long been a principal ingredient of fertilizers in the form of organic phosphates in natural fertilizers, such as manures, and as inorganic phosphates in commercial fertilizers. Phosphorus is an essential nutrient for the suc-

cessful growth of most vegetation and has been used in agriculture for many years to improve crop yields. Every crop grown takes nutrients from the soil to satisfy its own demand, and these must be replenished by natural or commercial fertilizers to avoid depletion of the soil's nutrient supply. Unfortunately, heavy rains and sudden spring run-off leach a large portion of the fertilizing elements from the soil and much of the fertilizer reaches the nearest stream for eventual delivery to lakes, rivers and oceans.

Detergents became popular in the late 1940's as a means of overcoming the combination of soap and hard water for laundry and other washing purposes. The early active ingredients were alkyl benzene sulfonates (ABS), which were good suds producers but not biologically degradable by sewage treatment plants. These became a major problem in the late 1950's when concentrations built up in lakes and rivers to the point of being covered with foam or suds. Such foaming has been observed in billows 15 to 20 feet high at the Barge Canal locks in New York State. This created a serious problem for drinking water supplies because the water treatment plants couldn't get rid of the foam either.

The manufacturers then fell back on the phosphates to ease the foam problem. Trisodium phosphate had been known for many years as an excellent cleansing material. The phosphates are likewise not degradable by biological activity, and they have been delivered to the lakes and rivers in the sewage treatment plant effluents where they perform their natural function of fertilization by enhancing algae and other aquatic growths. Algae and aquatic vegetation die at the end of their life cycle, settle to the bottom and decay, whereupon the phosphorus is converted from the organic to the inorganic form and is reported to rise to the surface to repeat its function in promoting more growth. This re-cycling process plus continual additions of phosphorus eventually lead to eutrophication of the body of water because of the depletion of dissolved oxygen used to decompose the dead vegetation. While there is sufficient oxygen dissolved in the water, organic matter will decompose with production of CO_2 and H_2O. When the dissolved oxygen has been depleted, CH_4 (methane) and CO_2 are produced, and septic conditions prevail.

Fly ash usually contains appreciable quantities of soluble hydroxides (sodium and potassium) in addition to gypsum ($CaSO_4$) and lime (CaO). The soluble hydroxides should tend to increase the pH of the water, and the calcium released from the lime and gypsum has been reported to combine well with phosphates to form complex calcium phosphate precipitates, which settle to the bottom mud of the lake or stream where the phosphate is held to prevent further re-cycling. However, it may be found that pH is actually reduced through other over-riding reactions.

In selecting fly ash for this experiment it is important to choose a source which produces ash low in phosphates but fairly high in gypsum and lime. Fly ash from sixteen sources has been reported to vary from zero to about 0.3% phosphorus. Tenney and Echelberger (Reference No. 1) reported using fly ash with zero phosphorus as (P_2O_5) and with 3.4% calcium (as CaO) in performing this experiment.

1. To simulate a column of water in a lake or river and to provide depth for settling, fill two 2-liter graduated cylinders with the polluted water.

2. Sprinkle 20 grams of dry fly ash on the surface of the water in one cylinder.

3. Allow fly ash to settle quietly for 24 hours.

4. Pipette or decant the required amount of water from each cylinder, as specified for the phosphates analyzer you are using.

5. Determine total phosphate concentrations of the treated and untreated waters.

6. Repeat, using other concentrations of fly ash per liter of water.

VII. Records and Evaluation of Data

1. Keep accurate and complete records of your observations and determinations for each test performed.

2. Plot turbidity, color, and phosphate vs. concentration of fly ash in the water, each on 10 × 10 or 20 × 20 linear graph paper.

VIII. References

1. Mark E. Tenney and Wayne E. Echelberger, Jr., Fly Ash Utilization in the Treatment of Polluted Waters; Second Ash Utilization Symposium, Pittsburgh, Pa., March 10–11, 1970.

2. Standard Methods for the Examination of Water and Wastewater; American Public Health Association, 1790 Broadway, New York, N.Y. 10019.

IX. Prepared by David J. Romano and Donald C. Hunter

EXPERIMENT NO. 36

Introduction to Noise Pollution Measurement

I. Object

1. To introduce the student to the problem of noise pollution.

2. To establish a quantitative relationship between noise sources and sound pressure levels.

II. Suitability and Usefulness

1. Can be used as a science field project.

2. Measurements can be made quantitatively if sound level measuring equipment is available, and qualitatively if not.

3. Increases awareness of the harmful effects of noise.

III. Theory

Noise may be defined as unwanted sound. Sound is produced by the transfer of mechanical vibration to air, and thus unwanted sound may be considered a form of air pollution. The vibration of an object moving back and forth disturbs air molecules nearby and starts them vibrating, producing a variation in atmospheric pressure. The disturbance spreads like the ripples on a pond when we toss in a pebble. Pressure disturbances in air spread at a speed of about 1100 feet per second. When they reach our ear drums, the drums start

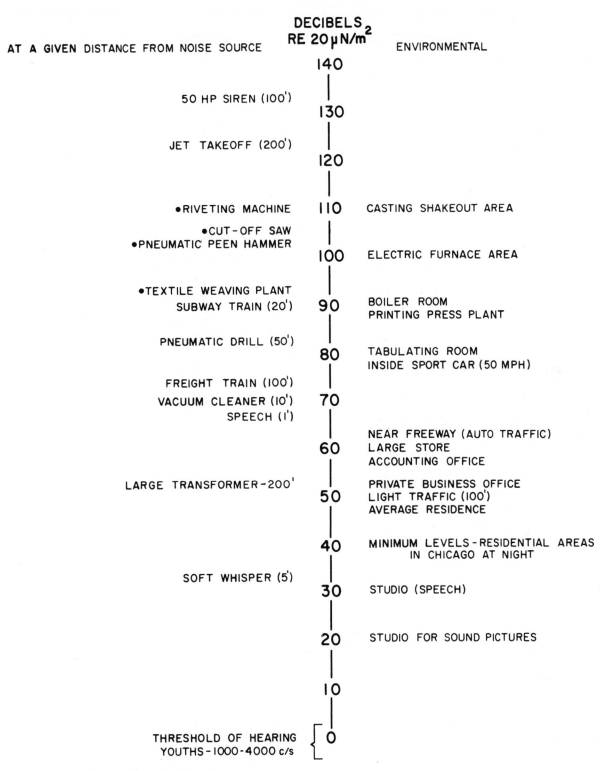

DECIBELS RE 20 $\mu N/m^2$

AT A GIVEN DISTANCE FROM NOISE SOURCE — 140 — ENVIRONMENTAL

50 HP SIREN (100') — 130

JET TAKEOFF (200') — 120

•RIVETING MACHINE — 110 — CASTING SHAKEOUT AREA

•CUT-OFF SAW
•PNEUMATIC PEEN HAMMER — 100 — ELECTRIC FURNACE AREA

•TEXTILE WEAVING PLANT
SUBWAY TRAIN (20') — 90 — BOILER ROOM / PRINTING PRESS PLANT

PNEUMATIC DRILL (50') — 80 — TABULATING ROOM / INSIDE SPORT CAR (50 MPH)

FREIGHT TRAIN (100')
VACUUM CLEANER (10') — 70
SPEECH (1')

— 60 — NEAR FREEWAY (AUTO TRAFFIC) / LARGE STORE / ACCOUNTING OFFICE

LARGE TRANSFORMER-200' — 50 — PRIVATE BUSINESS OFFICE / LIGHT TRAFFIC (100') / AVERAGE RESIDENCE

— 40 — MINIMUM LEVELS-RESIDENTIAL AREAS IN CHICAGO AT NIGHT

SOFT WHISPER (5') — 30 — STUDIO (SPEECH)

— 20 — STUDIO FOR SOUND PICTURES

— 10

THRESHOLD OF HEARING
YOUTHS-1000-4000 c/s — 0

•OPERATOR'S POSITION

FIG. 36-1

TYPICAL "A" WEIGHTED SOUND LEVELS MEASURED WITH A SOUND LEVEL METER. THESE VALUES ARE TAKEN FROM THE LITERATURE. SOUND LEVEL MEASUREMENTS GIVE ONLY PART OF THE INFORMATION USUALLY NECESSARY TO HANDLE NOISE PROBLEMS, AND ARE OFTEN SUPPLEMENTED BY ANALYSIS OF THE NOISE SPECTRA.

FROM HANDBOOK OF NOISE MEASUREMENT, GENERAL RADIO COMPANY

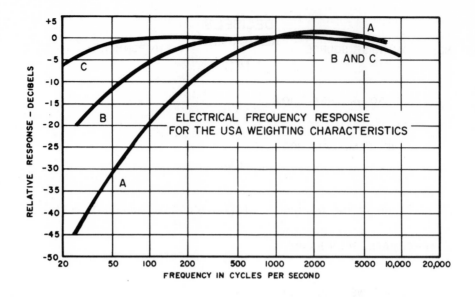

FIG. 36-2

FREQUENCY-RESPONSE CHARACTERISTICS IN THE USA STANDARD FOR SOUND-LEVEL METERS, SI.4, 1961.

FROM HANDBOOK OF NOISE MEASUREMENT, GENERAL RADIO COMPANY.

vibrating. Our complicated hearing mechanism then translates the ear drum vibrations into the sensation we call sound. The heavier or more violent these pressure vibrations are, the louder is the sound we hear.

Sound can also vary by tone or pitch, which is determined by the frequency at which the pressure vibrations occur. The occurrence from the start of one pressure vibration to the start of the next is known as a cycle. In sounds of high pitch or shrill tone, the vibrations occur more frequently than in sounds of low pitch. Thus, every tone can be identified by the frequency of its vibrations. We express this frequency in cycles per second (cps), or Hertz (Hz). The standard tone, middle A by which an orchestra tunes up before a concert, has a vibration frequency of 440 cycles per second, or 440 Hz.

People with normal hearing can usually hear and distinguish tones between frequencies of 30 Hz and 16,000 Hz. Some animals can hear tones not audible to the human ear. You are all familiar with the dog whistle, by which a dog can hear a shrill tone far beyond our range of perception.

The intensity of sound at any time is related to the sound pressure level. It is expressed in decibels, referred to zero decibels as the threshold intensity of sound which can be heard by youths with normal hearing in the frequency range of 1000 to 4000 Hz and which is the starting point for noise levels. More specifically, the threshold sound pressure level is defined as 20 micronewtons per square meter, 0.0002 dyne per square centimeter, or 0.0002 microbar. (The prefix "micro" means "one-millionth of" the stated unit of measure.)

Noise is a growing problem in our environment. The cities and countryside are afflicted because of the many existing noise sources, both mobile and stationary. Physicians warn that continued exposure to high noise levels can cause chronic loss of hearing. Noise can also interfere with communication, reduce work output, increase the frequency of errors and accidents, and fray our nerves.

The goal of all noise measuring instrumentation is to produce a number or value which indicates how the normal ear will respond to a sound. At present no single instrument completely achieves this goal. A sound level meter which measures sound pressure levels is an accepted instrument. Other instruments, using computer techniques for frequency analysis, produce more sophisticated results. We shall consider only the sound level meter in this experiment.

Noise Measurement

It is helpful to relate sound pressure levels to personal noise experience. Figure 36-1 lists typical sounds and their corresponding sound pressure levels. Such levels can be measured by the sound level meter. The instrument consists of a microphone to detect the sound pressure wave, an electronic amplifier to boost the signal level, a frequency weighting network, and an output meter calibrated to indicate sound pressure levels in decibels (dB). The sound level decibel (dB) values indicated are with reference to zero decibels, taken as the threshold or sound level of first perception of the human ear. The frequency weighting networks, which combine all frequencies with respect to the percentage of each, consists of three attenuating circuits which are described by the characteristics shown in Figure 36-2. The "A," "B," and "C" frequency weighting networks attenuate, or weaken, the electrical signal to the meter by the amounts shown on the graph in an attempt to duplicate what happens in the human ear. The meter will give essentially the same reading for all three networks when the frequency of the sound is above 1000 Hz. The "A" network will give the lowest reading (greatest attenuation), for frequencies below 1000 Hz which is most characteristic of the human ear. Sound levels in decibels measured on this frequency weighting network are indicated as dBA.

The sound pressure level dB values cannot be directly added or subtracted because of their logarithmic nature. For example, two noise levels of 80 decibels rather than 160 decibels. Computations for combining two dB levels (which are beyond the scope of this experiment) can be made by combining the actual pressures and then recalculating the dB value.

IV. Equipment

1. Sound pressure level meter, such as General Radio Co. No. 1561 or No. 1551-C.
2. The human ear can be used if a meter is not available. When using your ear, refer to Figure 36-1 so that you can assign approximate dBA values to noise levels.

V. Procedure

Survey your community, home, school and local environment to identify at least thirty noise sources. Using the "A" frequency weighting network, establish a sound level value in dBA, for each source by measurement or listening. Classify the noise source and sound with respect to its nature—whether mobile or stationary, steady or pulsating, annoying, interference with speech, or according to any other reactions. *Remember that long term exposure to sound levels greater than 90 dBA can produce hearing loss.*

VI. Records

Record your observations in an appropriate table. Discuss what might be done to reduce noise. Are all noise sources necessary? Do sounds have to be as loud as they are? What sound level is produced by many rock music groups?

VII. References

1. A. P. G. Peterson and E. E. Gross, Jr., Handbook of Noise Measurements, 6th Edition; General Radio Company, 1967.
2. Acoustics Handbook, Application Note 100; Hewlett Packard Company, November, 1968.

VIII. Prepared by Donald E. Gower

EXPERIMENT NO. 37

Construction of a Simple Sound Level Meter

I. Object

1. To construct a simple sound level meter suitable for measuring noise levels.

II. Suitability and Usefulness

1. Can be used to determine school and community noise levels in conjunction with the preceding experiment.

2. Can be used to demonstrate the measurement of noise levels at a school science fair.

3. Building a usable instrument for making sound level measurements will increase your self-confidence and feeling of accomplishment.

III. Background

Construction of the sound level meter illustrated in this experiment is not difficult, but requires close attention to detail and care in making the soldered connections. If you have worked with a radio or a record amplifier, you should find the requirements similar. The model illustrated was built in a Bakelite case $6\frac{3}{16}'' \times 3\frac{3}{4}'' \times 1\frac{15}{16}''$ high. You may use a larger case if you wish to provide more space for components and connections.

While more sophisticated instruments can be used on either the "A," "B," or "C" frequency weighting networks, this instrument for simplicity approximates the "A" network only.

Cost of parts should be well under $50.

IV. Equipment

Parts needed for construction of the sound level meter are as follows (refer to Figs. 37-1 and 37-4 for identification of parts):

1. B1, B2—9-volt battery (Eveready 216, or equivalent).

2. Capacitors:
   (a) C1—0.02 μf, 100-v disc.
   (b) C2—1 μf, 20-v electrolytic.
   (c) C3, C9—10 μf, 20-v electrolytic.
   (d) C4, C7—100 μf, 20-v electrolytic.
   (e) C5—0.05 μf, 100-v disc.
   (f) C6—100 $\mu\mu$f, 100-v disc.
   (g) C8—500 μf, 10-v electrolytic.

3. IC1—CA3018 or CA3018A integrated circuit (RCA).

4. M1—VU meter (Lafayette 99 F 50437).

5. Mic.—Miniature crystal microphone cartridge (Lafayette 99 F 45098).

6. Transistors
   (a) Q1, Q2—2N5089 transistor (Motorola).
   (b) Q3—2N3905 transistor (Motorola).
   (c) Q4—2N4126 transistor (Motorola).

7. Resistors: $\frac{1}{4}$ watt, 10% tolerance unless otherwise indicated. (Likewise, values are in ohms unless otherwise specified.)
   (a) R1—1 megohm.
   (b) R2—68,000 (5%).
   (c) R3, R10—100,000 (5%).
   (d) R4, R15, R18, R22—10,000.
   (e) R5—6,800 (5%).
   (f) R6—2,200 (5%).
   (g) R7—680 (5%).
   (h) R8—220 (5%).
   (i) R9—100 (5%).
   (j) R11—330 (5%).
   (k) R12—100.
   (l) R13—100,000.
   (m) R14—390,000.
   (n) R16—56,000 (5%).
   (o) R17—68,000.
   (p) R19—10.
   (q) R20, R24—2,200.
   (r) R21—15,000.
   (s) R23—100-ohm trimmer pot (IRC U-201R101B).

8. S1—3 pole, 11-position sub-miniature ceramic rotary switch (Centralab PS-106, Allied catalog #56 D 5306. $7.56 plus postage. Not listed in consumer catalog.)

9. S2—Normally open push-button switch (Switchcraft 951, or equiv.).

10. S3—SPDT miniature slide switch.

11. $6\frac{3}{8}'' \times 3\frac{3}{16}'' \times 1\frac{7}{8}''$ Bakelite utility case with aluminum panel. (Lafayette 99 F 62721, or equiv.).

12. Wire for connections
    a. Shielded microphone cable.
    b. #22 or #24 hook-up wire, insulated.

13. Aluminum sheet ($\frac{1}{32}''$ thick) for shield and microphone bracket (Fig. 37-5).

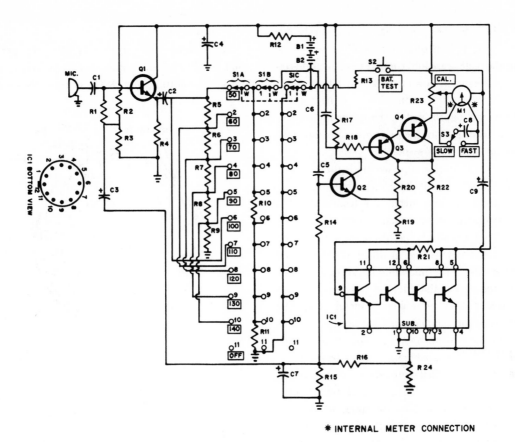

FIG. 37–1 WIRING DIAGRAM

* INTERNAL METER CONNECTION

14. Perforated circuit board, 3¼″ × 3¾″.

15. Flea clips.

16. Dry transfer lettering for labeling.

17. Double-sided foam tape to isolate microphone from case.

V. Tools

1. 35-watt soldering iron.

2. Chassis punch for meter.

3. Drill

4. Needle nose pliers.

5. Wire cutter.

6. Standard AC voltmeter or oscilloscope.

7. Any audio signal generator. (If not available locally, contact the nearest governmental industrial hygiene group on the possibility that they might have one you could use.)

VI. Procedure

A. Construction

Study the wiring diagram and the circuit board sketch carefully. The circuit layout is not difficult, but complete attention to detail is essential. The

following details should be given special attention:

1. Keep wire connections on the circuit board as short as possible.

2. Note that the input signal from the microphone to C1 is via shielded microphone cable.

3. Shielding of the circuit board is essential to eliminate interference at the input stage, and the aluminum shield must be connected to the ground bus on the circuit board. (The aluminum shield can be eliminated from the circuit board if an all-aluminum case is used.) The bottom of the shield facing the circuit board should be covered with plastic electrical tape to avoid possible shorting of the circuit to the grounded shield.

4. The specified VU meter has four screw terminals—two for the input signal and two for internal lamps; the latter are not used in the sound level meter. The two input terminals are also used for mounting the circuit board. A ⅜″ spacer is used on each of the two terminals to raise the board for clearance of selector switch S1.

5. Because the meter has a built-in bridge rectifier, it is necessary to drill a ³⁄₁₆″ hole in the meter case and connect two wires directly to the meter movement. The handiest points for making these connections are the rectifier terminals which lead to the meter movement. The other ends of the two wires are connected to the "fast-slow" switch S3.

6. The dial scale supplied with the meter is not used for sound level measurement. Trace or photocopy the meter face from Fig. 37-3 and glue this over the existing meter face.

7. To duplicate the performance of the sound level meter described in this experiment, you must use the microphone specified. The ground wire of the shielded cable must be connected to the microphone's metal case. The microphone should be physically isolated from the case to avoid pick-up of unwanted sound; double sided foam tape can be used.

8. If the specified transistors are not available, try substituting universal replacement transistors supplied by Sylvania, RCA, GE, etc. (Satisfactory performance was achieved with Sylvania's ECG-123A substituting for 2N5089 and ECG-159 substituting for 2N3905 and 2N4126.)

9. Label the positions of switch S1 as follows:

Position #1	50 (decibels)
#2	60
#3	70
#4	80
#5	90
#6	100
#7	110
#8	120
#9	130
#10	140
#11	OFF

10. Note that the three decks of switch S1 are labeled as follows on the wiring diagram:

Rear deck S1A
Middle deck S1B
Front deck S1C

11. Bracket (Fig. 37-5) holds microphone in place.

12. Drill several (about 24) ⅛″ holes through the end of the case directly in front of the microphone position.

B. Calibration

Set a signal generator at 1,000 cycles per second (1,000 Hz) and adjust its output level to 1 volt peak-to-peak (0.35 volt, RMS or root mean square,

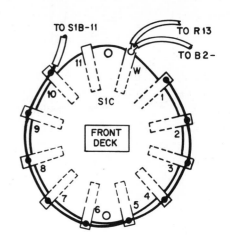

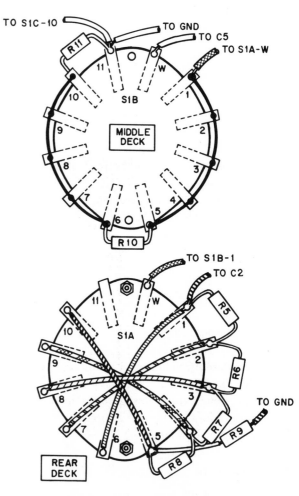

FIG. 37-2 DECKS OF SWITCH S1
Before installing it on panel, hold its shaft in vise and wire as shown. Front deck is nearest shaft.

as determined on a standard AC voltmeter or oscilloscope.) Set range selector switch S1 at 130 decibels (dB) and feed the signal through C1; do this by attaching one generator lead to the ground bus and the other lead to C1 at the point where the shielded cable from the microphone is connected to C1.

Adjust R23 for a "zero" dB reading on the meter.

Transistor gain may vary between individual units, and for this reason you may not be able to obtain a "zero" reading on the meter during calibration. Substitution of another transistor of the same number may increase the sensitivity sufficiently for calibration. (The transistor that let's you get a "zero" reading should be kept in the circuitry for operation.)

C. Operation

Before using the instrument, be sure to read the preceding experiment on the basics of sound level measurement.

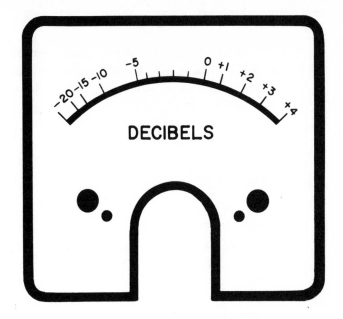

FIG. 37-3 Cut out scale above and paste over meters' scale. The black circles must also be cut for mounting holes and unused illuminating lamps.

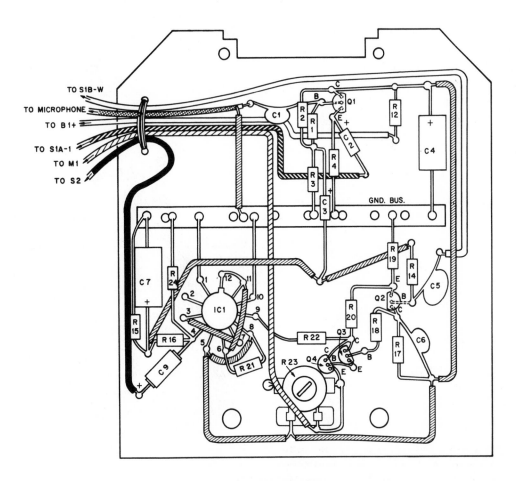

FIG. 37-4
SKETCH SHOWING WIRING OF CIRCUIT BOARD

Fig. 37-6. Photo at right shows upper side of circuit board, switch S1, batteries, microphone, and meter. Note wires connecting switch S3 to rectifier inside meter.

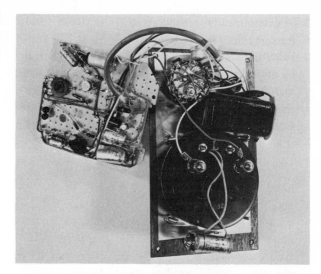

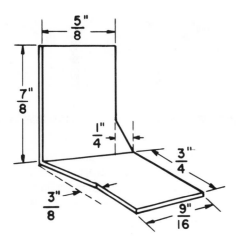

BRACKET

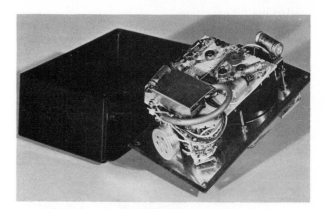

Fig. 37-7. Assembly before inserting in box.

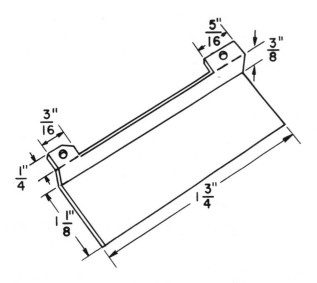

SHIELD

Fig. 37-5. Dimensions of bracket and shield used in model. Both are made of 1/32″ thick aluminum. Shield goes at top of board over Q1 as shown in photo.

Fig. 37-8. Sound level meter in use, indicating a sound level of 70−7.5 = 62.5 dBA.

Hold the instrument with its microphone pointing in the direction of the sound level to be measured.

The meter indicates sound levels above and below the setting of range selector switch S1. For example, if S1 is set at 80 dB and the meter pointer is at +4, the sound level is 84 dBA. If the meter pointer is at −3, the sound level is 77 dBA.

With rapidly repeating sounds, it is sometimes advantageous to determine an average sound level rather than try to follow rapid meter fluctuations. The "fast-slow" switch S3 in the slow position causes the meter to be highly damped with the result the pointer moves very slowly and indicates an average value for the fluctuating sound level.

To check the strength of the batteries, set switch S1 at 140 dB and press battery check switch S2. A meter reading between zero and +4 indicates the batteries are in good condition.

VII. References

1. Walt Henry, A Direct-Reading Sound Meter You Can Build; Electronics Illustrated, March 1971.

VIII. Acknowledgment

Inclusion of this experiment is made possible through the kindness of Electronics Illustrated.

IX. Prepared by Thomas J. Moran

EXPERIMENT NO. 38

Use of Solar Energy for Heat

I. Object

1. To demonstrate that useful heat can be produced from solar energy without production of air, water, or land pollution.

II. Suitability and Usefulness

1. Teaches students that the sun is an unlimited source of energy which can substitute for at least a portion of the carbonaceous and nuclear fuels used for the production of heat and power.

2. Makes a good project to demonstrate that useful heat can be gathered from the sun and utilized without producing pollution.

III. Theory

Ever since man first discovered fire, he has been relying on the combustion of carbonaceous fuels (grass, dung, fats, wood, coal, oil, and gas) to warm himself and cook his food. With the invention of the steam engine and later the electric power generator, he has also burned fuels to produce power. More recently nuclear fission has been used for power production. All of these fuels produce undesirable by-products which can foul the air, water and land, with subsequent detrimental effects on health and economic well-being. Falling water is

used with the water wheel for direct production of mechanical power and, including the rising and falling ocean tides, is being used with the turbine to produce electric power. The power developed by moving air has been used with the windmill. But the availability of falling water, useable tides, and wind is limited.

Our need for electric power has been expanding at an ever-increasing rate and is expected to double every ten years. Yet, in the scramble to keep up with demands for power to operate our industries and to heat and cool our homes, schools, and offices, we have largely overlooked our greatest source of energy—the sun. This has happened in spite of the fact that man has sought from time to time during past centuries to utilize this source of energy. It is said that Archimedes, around 200 B.C., burned the sails of the Roman fleet at Syracuse by focusing mirrors on them. Throughout the ages, man has used solar energy to preserve his food by drying and to produce salt and other chemicals by evaporation of sea water. Some women still insist on sun-dried laundry. Solar energy is used for heating and cooking in remote areas of the world and in a few instances for home heating in more developed countries. A small solar power generator made it possible for men to survive and communicate by radio and television from the moon.

Although the sun's energy is partially absorbed by the atmosphere and less and less gets through the more we pollute the air, it has been estimated that each square mile of the earth's surface could produce 180,000 kilowatts of power, at only a 10% conversion efficiency, from the small portion that does get through. For example, if we had solar power generating plants covering the 3.2 million acres laid waste by strip mining we could be producing about 1 billion kilowatts of power from them. This is about 100 times the power New York City is expected to need in the year 2,000. Another possibility would be satellite solar power stations transmitting power to earth-bound receivers by microwave. Being above our atmospheric envelope, the losses from atmospheric absorption of solar radiation and cloud cover would be avoided.

While these examples of power generation may seem fanciful now, the technology is known and they are within the realm of future feasibility. We can perhaps broaden interest in developing greater use of solar energy by experimenting with a very small portion of the sun's radiation to demonstrate that water can be heated without concomitant production of pollution. On the other hand, if we burn oil or gas for the same purpose, we produce polluting substances at home and, if we use electricity, the local power plant is required to burn more fuel with the extra pollution occurring there.

The housewife will probably ask how water can be heated by solar energy at night and during stormy weather. It can't. But, by storing solar heated water in a 100-gallon insulated tank, a large part of the problem can be solved. If this doesn't supply the family's demand for hot water, the conventional oil, gas, or electric water heater goes to work until the sun can again take over its job.

Man has inhabited space-ship earth for thousands of years, yet most of the fuels and minerals mined or pumped from the earth have been removed and consumed within the last century. Unless conservation of fuel and mineral resources starts soon, our descendants may have rough sledding. It is up to us to keep experimenting and persuading people around us to try using clean forms of energy which do not foul the environment or deplete our resources.

Let's proceed with our experiment, first trying very simple and primitive methods of heating water by solar energy and gradually working up to more sophisticated methods and equipment.

IV. Equipment

A. First experiment
    1. Garden hose, 25 to 50 feet long.
    2. Thermometer.
    3. Watch.

B. Second experiment
    1. Large white enamel dishpan; two required.
    2. Black plastic sheeting, large enough to line one pan.
    3. Glass or rigid clear plastic ($\frac{1}{8}$" to $\frac{1}{4}$" thick) large enough to completely cover a pan; two required.
    4. Thermometer.
    5. Watch.

C. Third experiment
    1. Water-proof, clear plastic bag such as Mylar, about 3 feet square, with the outside of one surface painted black. (The black surface absorbs heat.) Inlet and outlet tubing should be provided at opposite edges of the bag. The bag should be sealed to prevent leakage of water. (Mylar can be sealed to itself with heat applied by a hot iron.)
    2. Small tank for storing water, with inlet at top and outlet at bottom. (A 5-gal. jerry-can may be used.) Outside of tank should be covered with a blanket of insulation, such as glass fiber, to retard cooling of heated water. Tank should have a loose fitting cover *or* other vent as a safety measure in case too much heat is developed.
    3. Plastic or copper tubing to convey water from bag to tank and from tank to bag.
    4. Thermometer.
    5. Watch or clock.

D. Fourth experiment
    1. Heat absorber, consisting of looped copper tubing ($\frac{1}{4}$" or $\frac{3}{8}$") in a shallow glass or plastic-covered wood or aluminum box. The box should be about 3 feet square (9 sq. ft.) × 4 inches deep with bottom and side walls completely insulated. The tubing should be looped back and forth, using a bending tool to avoid flattening the tubing at the bends,

Fig. 38-1. Demonstration model of a solar water heater, built and used successfully by New York State Department of Environmental Conservation.

and should then be soldered over its complete length to a flat sheet of copper. The tubing and both sides of the copper sheet should then be painted flat black for maximum heat absorption. Lay the assembly of copper sheet and tubing in the box with the tubing underneath. Provide fittings on both ends of copper tubing which extend through two walls of the box.

2. Tank as in C.

3. Tubing as in C for circulating water from the tank to the absorber and back to the tank.

4. Thermometer.

5. Watch or clock.

V. Procedure

A. First experiment

Lay the garden hose on the lawn at about 8 AM on a clear, warm day. Fill the hose and determine water temperature at the nozzle and air temperature. Leave the hose in this position all day and determine air and water temperatures every half hour.

B. Second experiment

At about 8 AM, set the two dishpans on the roof of your school where they will receive the full rays of the sun all day. Line one pan with the black plastic sheeting. Fill both pans from a cold water faucet. Determine air and water temperatures. Cover both pans with the glass or plastic. Determine outdoor air temperature and water temperature in each pan every half hour.

C. Third experiment

Assemble the apparatus on your school roof in the morning of a clear day, with the heat absorbing bag lying on the roof with its clear surface upward and tilted toward the sun. Mount the tank to the north and a little higher. Connect the tubing to form a closed loop with the bag and tank, so that water will flow from the bottom of the tank to the bottom of the bag and from the top of the bag to the top of the tank. The density of water becomes less as its temperature rises. Thus warmer water will rise through the heat absorber and flow to the top of the tank, to be replaced by cooler water from the bottom of the tank. Keep the bag shaded until it is full of water.

Add water to the tank until tank, bag, and tubing are full. Record the number of gallons required. Replace the tank cover. Remove the shading material so that the bag is in full sunlight.

Determine and record outdoor air temperature and temperature of water near the top and bottom of the tank when you start and every half-hour thereafter.

D. Fourth experiment

Assemble the apparatus on the roof of your school in the morning of a clear day, with the heat absorber tilted to the sun. Greatest heat absorption will occur when the sun's rays are perpendicular to the glass or plastic cover. Keep the absorber shaded until its tubing is filled with water. Mount the tank to the north and a little higher than the absorber. Connect the tubing to form a closed loop with the absorber and tank, so that water will flow from the bottom of the tank to the bottom of the absorber and from the top of the absorber to the top of the tank. Water circulation will be as described for the third experiment.

Fill the tank and all tubing with cold water. Record the number of gallons required. Replace the tank cover. Remove the shading material so that the absorber is in full sunlight.

Determine and record the following temperatures when you start and every half-hour thereafter:

    1. Outdoor air.
    2. Air above copper sheet in absorber.
    3. Water near top of tank.
    4. Water at bottom of tank.

Duration of Each Experiment

Each experiment should be planned to proceed from about 8:30 a.m. until about 4:00 p.m.; shorter duration may be possible if water temperature throughout the tank reaches 140°F sooner.

Caution: In the third and fourth experiments, water entering the top of the tank may be near the boiling point. Don't touch it.

VI. Records

Keep neat and complete records of all of your observations.

VII. Problems

1. For each experiment, determine the heat input in Btu/square foot/hour needed to heat the water to 140°F or to the highest water temperature you were able to achieve. (A Btu, or British thermal unit, is the amount of heat required to raise the temperature of one pound of water 1°F. A gallon of water weighs 8.33 lbs.)

$$Btu/ft^2/hr =$$

$$\frac{\text{lbs. water} \times (°F \text{ end} - °F \text{ start})}{\text{area of absorber surface} \times \text{hours}}$$

2. If it takes too long to increase water temperature as much as desired, what changes in your apparatus would you propose? Discuss with your teacher.

3. Can you get enough heat absorption on a cloudy day to increase water temperature?

4. From your own experiments, can you estimate the area of heat collecting surface and the volume of water storage your family would need for an adequate supply of solar heated water?

5. Other possible practical uses for solar energy are suggested for class discussion—for example, solar cooling systems, solar powered vehicles, and satellite solar power generating stations. Supplemental reading of books available in your school or state library is suggested.

6. Would it be practical to pipe a solar water heater in series or in parallel with your family's gas, oil, or electric water heater at home and achieve the dual advantage of reducing pollution and cost of heating water? How would you go about it? (*CAUTION:* Don't start any construction without the permission of your teacher *and* your parents. The author and editors can't accept responsibility for any plumbing surprises.)

VIII. References

1. Peter E. Glaser, A New Look at the Sun; The Conservationist, New York State Department of Environmental Conservation, June–July 1971.

2. D. S. Halacy, Jr., Fabulous Fireball; The Macmillan Company, 1957.

IX. Prepared by Donald C. Hunter. Demonstration model (see Fig. 38-1) built by John M. Joyce.

SPECIAL NOTE TO STUDENTS

All students, whether intending to pursue higher education or not, are encouraged to learn as much as possible about the condition and needs of the environment in which we all live. A first requisite is the development of an awareness of people and situations around us, because an understanding of the total environment and its needs requires the ability to observe and evaluate the effects of the actions of each and every one of us on the various segments of the total environment. Our environment consists of atmosphere, water, soil, mineral resources, insects, microscopic organisms, vegetation, wild and domestic land animals, marine life, birds, and people, plus our homes, factories, offices, stores, schools, and transportation facilities. All must exist in harmony on this finite planet, Earth, according to the first law of ecology which states that "everything is connected to everything else." Therefore, each of us should study and attempt to understand the laws of ecology so that a life of harmony can continue.

This does not mean that we should not control pests, such as rats and houseflies, but it does suggest that we should perhaps not attempt to completely eradicate them without an understanding of their total effect on the environment. It suggests that we should not try to eliminate all sulfur dioxide from the atmosphere while leaving nitrogen oxides unchecked; sulfur dioxide, when present, reduces ozone to oxygen, whereas unlimited ozone, under solar radiation, could combine with nitrogen oxides to form high concentrations of oxidants injurious to vegetation and potentially dangerous to man. It suggests that we should conserve mineral resources and look to our waste products, including solar radiation, for useful mineral and energy content so that as much as possible of Earth's resources will be available to people of the future. We should consider that each generation holds the environment in trust for the generations to come.

Those of you favoring science subjects will find, after educating yourselves in engineering, biological science, or medicine, that many careers in management of environmental quality are open to you. In pursuing such further education, a thorough understanding of ecology in its true sense should be a definite goal, and elective courses in the physical and social sciences should be chosen judiciously to achieve it. Governmental control agencies, educational institutions, and industrial organizations are usually looking for young people who are thoroughly prepared.

Whether you become a worker, a homemaker, a business man, or a professional, we wish you the best of success in a harmonious environment.

Donald C. Hunter, P.E.
Henry C. Wohlers, Ph.D.
Editors

NOTES AND OBSERVATIONS

NOTES AND OBSERVATIONS

NOTES AND OBSERVATIONS

NOTES AND OBSERVATIONS